Whispers Amongst the Trees
An Introspective Look at Life on the Oregon Coast

An Anthological Work by
Sterncastle Writer's Collective

Find more books, buy sweet merch, and support indie publishing:
www.sterncastlepublishing.org/shop

© Sterncastle Publishing 2023

Published by: Sterncastle Publishing
1682 N. Coast Highway, Newport, OR 97365
sterncastlepublishing.org
community@sterncastlepublishing.org

ISBN: 978-1-960120-09-0 (Paperback)
        978-1-960120-10-6 (Ebook)

Library of Congress Control Number: 2023950231

This collection is dedicated to the Oregon Coast, its past, its present, and its future. May all who arrive on these sacred shores respect and protect this stunning and magnificent place.

Foreword

There is a unique place on the edge of the world. A place that many have visited but where few actually live. A place where a population of 10,000 constitutes a city, where big box stores and chain restaurants are few and far between. A place where one can breathe deeply and where the pristine air which fills up one's lungs comes in with a pleasant aroma of piney and floral essence, if not a hint of briny sea salt.

That place is the Oregon Coast.

For 363 miles from scenic Astoria to serene Brookings, the Oregon Coast offers unparalleled natural beauty. Majestic sites including Haystack Rock, Devil's Punchbowl, Sea Lion Caves, the Florence Dunes, and some of the world's most photographed lighthouses line these shores.

Yet somehow for all the wonders it possesses, the Oregon Coast has been passed over by generations of people seeking a home close to the shore. As the masses flocked to California and Washington for a taste of the beach life, the Oregon Coast remained, unsullied, and just as spectacular as ever. Somehow this slice of paradise, where windswept evergreens overlook dramatic black cliffs above churning blue waters, has remained "semi-rural" by government designation.

You may find yourself wondering how a place with so much inherent charm could be so readily overlooked by those searching in earnest for a place with these very qualities. I believe that it is that very wild grandeur of the place which is the culprit.

While logging, fishing, farming, and foraging have long constituted the economic lifeblood of this place, and still do to a large extent, for almost a century and a half it was only the bravest, heartiest, and most determined who were able to eke out a living in these remote reaches.

Consider if you will that until the New Deal projects of the 1930's came about, much of this coastline was without proper roads. For instance, in 1912 a group of businessmen seeking to boost local tourism took the first automobile trip from Newport to what would one day become Lincoln City. The trek of just 25 miles took them over 23 hours up steep, slippery slopes and along soft, sandy beaches.

At one point, cheese from the world renowned Tillamook Creamery reached markets in Portland not via roads, but by boat because the journey overland was just that arduous.

The remoteness of the place resulted in a lack of modern conveniences including access to sufficient healthcare, universities, nightlife, and more. The inaccessibility was enough to ward off many who were relegated to getting their dose of coastal magic through day trips or annual vacations.

However, for those possessed of the constitution to make a go of life here, a unique culture and way of life developed. Neighbors became connected in a way that many communities never experience because they were reliant on one another for their survival. The demands of life on the edge engendered a populace who was sturdy, resolute, and indomitable. Possessed of a will to live which drove them onward through adversity, and a sense of humor that kept them sane through it all. Even today, visitors will note a peculiar ambience of camaraderie and kindness here that is uncommon elsewhere.

In this anthology we seek to celebrate the rugged allure of the Oregon Coast and the unassailable spirit of those who call it home. While primarily fictitious, the works that grace this volume capture an essential truth about who we are, what we believe, why we have come here, and why we remain in this place.

Through tales laced with humor, horror, hope, humility, and honesty we present to you as complete as has ever been offered a look into the minds of we "Coasties." With these stories we seek to inspire you to one day trek the coast road and find your own piece of paradise here. May your memories of the place blend with ours, and remain forever, like whispers amongst the trees.

-   Don Gomez
    Publisher, Sterncastle Publishing

Table of Contents

Of the Mist

By Kyra Blank

I am a child of the mist.
My soul was born from
The branches of the trees that
Kissed my face as I pushed
Through them.

The light in my smile was
borrowed from the sun on
a warm rock beach while
I hunted crawdads in the shallow.

I grew like the trees that
Border the river. Strong, tall,
Proud.
My roots are deep in the
bedrock of this place, so deep
I can't know if the soil holds
Me here, or if I hold it.

My comfort lies in the
Sounds of this place.
My mind was
Sculpted from the calls of
Geese or the cry of a lamb.

My soul finds its peace
between blades of grass,
while I lay, peering through
to glimpse the world anew.

Bigfoot Saves Jesse

By Linoa Linette

January 11, 2012
Rocky Creek Viewpoint – Depoe Bay

Harsh winds clashed against the body of the van, but no amount of this persistent rattling could shake Jesse from his trance. It was one that he had entered time and time again, ever consuming him the moment his head would make contact with her pillow. Though his cramped surroundings were gradually beginning to clutter with the evidence of life ever since he had bought the cumbersome vehicle, this soft station to which he always returned was the only proof in his possession that Sophie had ever existed. He inhaled deeply, hoping to summon some remnants of his wife's unique perfumes, and yet, time had only rendered its impressions fainter by the day. Rather, it was beginning to transmogrify, taking on that distinctive, offensive cloy of must that always seemed to eventually seep its way into everything on the Oregon coast.

What does she look like now? ...Now that she's been in the ground for another day?

His eyes grew flat against this morbid consideration and he coiled tighter in his makeshift bed. Upon having driven away from her grave for the final time, in this very vehicle, he still couldn't shake the feeling that he had done something wrong; that he had simply abandoned her there in the dirt, like somehow her remains could summon feelings of isolation, fear and betrayal. Further racking at his guilt was the recollection that she always wished she could have seen the ocean for herself, and relentlessly, these waves did roar. The wind furiously pounded at the windows as though to never let him forget this.

With another change in the wind, thicker raindrops exploded against the narrow window panes above his head. It would seem that

2

everything about this untamed environment was demanding his attention, and upon failing to gain it, its outrage was only accelerating.

Certainly, the dramatic features of the coast did rival those of the Idaho deserts; he often thought back on their yawning valleys and fragrant sagebrush, but something about these memories always arrived flat and colorless to his mind. He had joked with Sophie that the West was a bit of an alien place; that the mountains encompassing Boise were like the walls of a wide crater, similar to those dimpling the moon, and possessive they were, containing its inhabitants like the ill-fated cattle imprisoned in the nearby farms. But no, not them; they would be different. They would get away from there someday.

Yet here and now on this angry coast, the world had shattered open into ragged rock and abstract cliff faces, generously spilling forth its naked clay into the clamoring sea. Lush, contorted, and windswept bluffs were ever collapsing into that merciless expanse, and so vast and devouring was this ocean that it perpetually unraveled into violent voids.

A whistle buoy hauntingly wailed between the gusts of wind somewhere, beyond the unusually open peninsula on which his van was parked.

Maybe I'll just try to go to sleep…

He exhaled, and the fog of his hoppy breath was eager to join the must and brine always smothering him into place. Before his nose, and twitching with every disturbance of the air, the sight of a familiar strand of hair, still woven in the pillowcase, blurred against his reddening eyes. They reluctantly sealed shut, and against the dark surface of their lids, he tried to summon Sophie's face again. Though it flickered across his memory with varying shapes and light, like her aroma, it was starting to become distant with time. His brow knit with shame.

How could I be starting to forget that face?

Memories of his hands, furiously tearing up photographs in wild fits, forced their way to the forefront of his mind and he whimpered.

The nearby clashing of aluminum cans mercifully pulled him from the spiral. With his eyes snapping back into the shape of life, he sat up swiftly and peered through the window. Past the distortions of the branching rain, he could make out a familiar, humanoid shape, hunched and rifling through the bag of trash he'd earlier discarded.

"Ugh…" He grimaced and massaged the weary muscles of his face, starting and ending with the corners of his eyes. *This fucking guy again…*

His legs swung over his nest of shirts and blankets, and through empty beer cans, he clumsily ducked his way toward the sliding door. He tugged it open loudly, hoping that any suggestion of aggression would coax this person into scattering, but it did not.

Instead, he found that the man was shamelessly shoulders deep in the loudly collapsing bag. Smirking, Jesse cruelly mused that he sought to crawl inside it for shelter, but further curious was the vagrant's naked feet; dirtied, scabbed, and poorly tattooed from whatever journey Jesse didn't dare try to imagine.

Once more ol' Bigfoot emerges from his cave and comes stumbling out of the woods.

Further humoring the joke, however callous, Jesse peered toward the nearby trees that bordered the empty highway. Against the wind, they bristled anxiously but stood with such stature that he thought they might be reciprocating his gaze. Their trunks bent forward as though to steal a closer look, but winds soon ebbing, the whistle buoys wailed louder, and everything snapped back into place.

Exhaling the wet air stiff through his nostrils, Jesse folded his arms and shifted his weight. He shielded his mouth briefly before finally speaking up, "Hey, man."

His voice betrayed him with hesitance. Rolling his eyes, he tried again, "Hey. Look-- Can I help you or something?"

This individual, cloaked in a mud-stained raincoat, not unlike the texture of the trash bag, merely ignored him and continued to dig. Irked at this lack of acknowledgment, Jesse sighed more audibly this time.

Seriously... who does this guy think he is?

Aggravated, he blurted out, "You know-- Every damn night, you're out here, making a mess of my trash. Like, if you want food or something-- shit, even a beer or whatever, you could just ask me, man. I'll help you out. Just quit trashing the place."

The figure's head turned slowly, but completely, revealing to Jesse a face mottled with dirt and steeped by age or wear, he couldn't quite tell. *I'm not without sympathy...* Jesse frowned. *But still...this is getting to be a bit ridiculous.*

Undeterred, Jesse's head swiveled in an attempt to coax some sort of response from the man, but upon failing to receive one yet again, he flailed and snapped, "What're you? Deaf?"

Signalling comprehension for what seemed to be the first time, the man's eyes narrowed indignantly. After squirreling away a couple of larger wine bottles into his plastic satchel, the man upended the whole trash bag before discarding it into the grass. Stunned, Jesse watched on as cans and wrappers unfurled around the van with an incoming curl of wind.

"Fuck you," the stranger spat, and with that, he simply walked away. He crossed the highway, and climbed the hill back into the trees, which seemed to quake and twirl with a silent, stifled laughter. Blinking hard, Jesse lowered his head, and with his hands pinned snugly beneath his armpits, all he could do at that moment was flatly stare at the array of garbage, playfully twirling in circles around his soaking feet. The growing puddle rippled around his bare toes as he wriggled them with realization.

Yeah. You're right – Fuck me, I guess…

Eventually, and with a shake of his head, he turned and receded into the confines of his van.

Forget it. Whatever… It's tomorrow's problem now…

January 12, 2012
Rocky Creek Viewpoint – Depoe Bay

Before Jesse's eyes had even opened to the light of the aging afternoon, a dull pain beneath his brow greeted his consciousness first. Rolling over, he grimaced and wrapped the pillow tight around his head. Though he inhaled, his nostrils filled with must again.

Please don't leave me like this…

He curled a little tighter.

Sophie, I'm --

The clattering of cans from outside rang loud, even through the density of the cushion's down. He tensed.

For real…?

Angrily pursing his lips, Jesse whipped the blanket from his legs and arose from the bench with a stumble. Yanking open the door, he emerged with such fury that his feet met the ground with another clumsy twist. Finger already cocked, he snapped, "Look, you asshole--"

He paused, befuddled to find nothing there. His brow knit, and stupidly, his head swiveled both ways to take in the peninsula. Gray and murky were the skies as though to perpetuate morning forever, and by now, unfamiliar cars gathered along the lookout. Briefly, he locked eyes with a young woman from across the parking lot, though she immediately recoiled to conceal her disgust.

Perplexed, Jesse switched back to the trash again. *I guess it must have been the wind...and I just burst out here screaming like a crazy person... Unsurprising.*

Exhaling, he knelt and collected the first few cans. stacked them up brusquely alongside the tire, all the while cursing beneath his breath about the 'stupid bastard from the forest'. He reached next for the torn, soaked trash bag, but upon its separation from the ground, it ballooned into a strange shape and squirmed. In the time it took for him to register this anomaly, the bag began to violently wretch, shake, and twist in all directions.

"What the-- hell?!"

In his panic, he dropped the bag and stepped away. It was still for only a moment before contorting into even wilder shapes, further confirming the presence of life.

Helplessly, he glanced toward the other end of the lookout, and fretted, *I'm really going to have to fight a raccoon in front of these people, aren't I?*

The bag toppled and rolled, with its plastic spiking against the shape of its inhabitant's desperate attempts to punch their way to freedom.

Should I get a stick... find a rock? Just... walk away?

The lip of the bag folded open, and guided by the light, a small, round head began to cautiously rise above the plastic. It was predictably furry, and yet, the colorful, clashing patterns of this creature did not quite match Jesse's expectations. Flitting its balding ears, the animal began to process its surroundings, before whipping its head around to identify the source of the shadow in which it had arrived. There, the pitiful creature crouched, froze, and simply stared at Jesse with wild, dilating eyes.

Oh...It's just a stupid cat...

Face scrunching, Jesse waved aggressively at the animal and grunted, "Shoo! Go on, get out of here!"

To his frustration, the stray quickly scurried beneath the van's chassis. Bracing himself against the filthy vehicle, he lowered himself to peek underneath, all the while failing to notice the black patrol car slowly crawling in his direction. Locking eyes with the cat, now contently curled alongside the furthest tire, Jesse hissed sharply in another vain attempt to scare it away. Still, the nearby slamming of a car door did not seem to fully register against his ear.

"God damn it," Jesse cussed beneath his breath and pinned his long, greasy hair to the back of his neck.

"Excuse me. Ma'am?"

Lips pursing, Jesse stretched his other arm long beneath the vehicle and wagged it toward the cat. Startled, the animal shirked to create distance before curling around the tire to peek at him from the other side.

Following another moment of observation, the police officer cleared his throat, and more forcefully beckoned, "Hey. You. Up here."

It wasn't until the officer's radio crackled that Jesse jolted and peeked around his shoulder. His stunned, wide-eyed expression prompted the young officer to chuckle, but quickly becoming serious again, he gestured vaguely to the van and declared, "You can't park this here."

Forgetting about the cat, Jesse reluctantly rose to meet the officer's eye. Scratching his head awkwardly, he started, "Well, uh, I wasn't--"

"We got a call this morning about a bunch of litter," the officer interjected. "I'm going to have to ask you to leave."

Jesse's face twisted with offense as images of the homeless man flashed throughout his thoughts, but before he could formulate a protest, the officer went on, "Are you able to move this thing, or what?"

A breeze pushed a can into the front of the officer's shoe. After scanning the ground, he added, "And, are you fit to drive?"

"Uh..." Jesse's brow lifted high and his eyes fluttered. "Yeah. I'm good. I can move it..."

"Okay." Chewing on his cheek, the officer nodded and took a moment to think. "Well, I'll tell you what... Since you're being pretty cooperative, I'll ignore the overnight parking... But, I have to give you a ticket at least for the littering. Think you could get this all cleaned up before you go, too?"

Expression darkening, Jesse brooded, *I'm going to kill that damn homeless guy.*

"Yes, sir..."

His attention started to migrate toward the trees, until the officer asked him, "Can I see your driver's license? For good measure, I'm going to ask you to take a field sobriety test as well."

Snapping out of it, Jesse grimaced again and nodded. Rubbing his eyes, he mumbled, "Yeah, okay... My I.D. is in the van though. Do you mind if I go in and grab it?"

"Yeah, sure."

As though attached to his shadow, the officer followed Jesse closely as he rounded the van and climbed back into the cabin. More curious than suspicious, the officer leaned forward to better inspect the cramped space, and with such intrigue reflecting in his voice, he asked Jesse, "So, you really live in this thing?"

Against the question, Jesse paused and squinted. *Live...? I'd hardly call it living...*

Throwing aside a pair of torn jeans, he answered cautiously, "Yeah... I do." His hand dipped into another empty pocket. "... But, it's temporary."

"Huh."

Though it bothered Jesse to watch the officer deliberately sniff at the interior, he was grateful that such aromas of mold did not result in any sort of further discussion. With his hand latching to the leather spine of his wallet, he tugged it free and announced, "Here..."

The officer accepted it, although his attention seemed to be trapped elsewhere. Pointing toward the counter, he smirked and inquired, "What's your cat's name?"

Jesse's head swiveled, only to immediately lock eyes with the stray now withdrawing its oily head from a mug of stagnant water. His face indecisively traded expressions of surprise, irritation, and disgust, before he feebly answered, "That's not my cat..."

"Really? Doesn't seem that way to me," the officer chuckled. "Kinda looks like my mom's cat though..."

After briefly scanning the card, he fanned it thoughtfully against his palm before backing away from the doorway. "Well, Mr. Boise, why don't you just step back out here and sit tight for me while I run this real quick, alright? Then I'll make sure you're okay to get out of here."

Jesse struggled to break his attention from the cat, but ultimately, he was inclined to preserve his freedom, however disenchanting. Chin dipping, he sighed in compliance and followed the officer.

"Yes, sir."

"Ugh, c'mon man..."

Upon the illumination of the brake lights before him, Jesse grumbled obscenities beneath his breath. Pressing his foot against the pedal, the van lurched forward, with its front bumper encroaching on the beaten-up car swerving across the line ahead of them.

This idiot's just doing it on purpose at this point... He rubbed at his eyes before dropping his hand on the wheel with some force. *Then again... Where do I need to be so badly? I suppose it's just as well...*

"After all, 'fuck me', right?"

He put more weight upon the brake, allowing the van to glide a bit more smoothly around the curve. Habitually, his eyes switched onto the rearview mirror and he squinted. Behind his head and catching his attention, he could see the cat thoughtlessly reciprocating his stare from its perch upon the counter. It leaned in tandem with the turn and straightened as the road did as well, all the while tapping its tail in some kind of silent, well-practiced rhythm.

I gotta do something about this...

Emerging from the hills, the forest broke away into open cliffs and sprawling, silver beaches, sporadically freckled with the suggestion of hunched-over beachcombers. The van soon came upon a wide pull-out and slowing to a crawl, Jesse eased the tires onto the gravel. Just as the vehicle fully separated from the road, there erupted a blaring horn from behind. Flinching, he turned to look through the window, just in time to see a low-lying sports car angrily charge over a dip in the rolling, patchwork highway.

Grumbling, he cussed, "What's the matter with people?"

Exhaling, he yanked off his seat belt and cracked open the door beside him. Upon hopping out, he swiveled, and couldn't help but take in the impressive scenery he was trying to leave behind. He smirked, briefly considering that the hills of Cape Foulweather vaguely resembled an alligator, but impatiently, a cold raindrop tapped at the ball of his nose, as though to remind him of why he had even stopped. Snapping out of his nonsensical musings, he circled the van and pried open the sliding door.

"Alright buddy, here's your stop."

The cat tipped its head curiously.

Mirroring this gesture, but adding a swing of his arm, Jesse once more tried to coax the animal into leaving. "C'mon."

Upon failing to receive any sort of reaction, he huffed and took hold of the opening in preparation to propel himself toward it. "That's it--"

Perking to attention, the cat whipped around and leaped from the counter. It landed easily with a soft thump, and cast Jesse one last glance, before hissing and slinking its way into the narrow space beneath the driver's seat.

"Are you serious? ..."

Grimacing, Jesse stepped back again and pinched the bridge of his nose.

What am I going to do about this?

His arm curled back beneath the other and against a humid breeze, he squeezed himself to produce warmth. Despite the quickening rainfall, all he could do in that moment was simply stand there, and brood over his options, most of them bleak. It wasn't until movement occurred in his peripheral that his head turned and he looked on toward the cape again. Though he wasn't sure why, the familiar sight of the homeless man, ambling barefoot along the highway, bag in tow, drew from him a singular, dry laugh.

Boy this guy sure is everywhere, isn't he?

Unconsciously, he wriggled his toes within the comfort of his shoes.

If I didn't know any better, I'd say he was following me. Jesse's gaze shifted onto thin air instead as he reflected on the strange events of the past couple of days. Brow lifting, he conceded, *then again... who am I to judge anymore? We're both just out here... trying to get by.*

Jesse peered back into the van, and though it appeared empty, he could feel the cat's wide stare returning his own from its new hiding place. Producing his keys from his pocket, he sighed deeply and relented, "Alrighty then, 'Bigfoot' ... Let's go find a place to lay our heads..."

January 13, 2012
Newport

A warm presence adhering to the shape of his head roused Jesse from his sleep. His eyes peeled open, and fleetingly, he anticipated that he would hear Sophie's voice. Just as he was grappling with the inconsistencies between his want and reality, another voice, inhuman but equally demanding in shape flooded his ear and startled him fully into lucidity.

He shot up and searched the blankets with panic. It was then that the cat, arching its back, entered his vision and stomped its way onto his lap. It smoothed against his torso in a small circle, before pointing its golden eyes at him and stretching its face into a wide yowl. *What do you want?*

Despite not vocalizing the question, the cat howled in response. Jesse's eyes shifted across its grimy features in search of an answer, until it occurred to him, "Oh... You're hungry."

Purring affirmatively, the cat bounced off the edge of the bed and wandered toward the narrow space meant to resemble a kitchenette. Jesse was slow to follow, but groaning, he eventually arose and ducked his way toward the cupboards.

"What do you little bastards even like, huh?"

He grimaced wearily, prying open a cabinet door. Jostled from transit, the cans within tumbled forth, some into his grasping hands, but the rest loudly rolled across the floor. Startled, the cat flung itself onto the counter, where it watched Jesse tediously rearrange them back into a stack. Upon retrieving the last one, Jesse tossed it once in rotation and paused to read its label.

Glancing at Bigfoot, he thought to ask, "You like chili? Hm? Would that do?"

The cat curiously returned his stare, but offered no further reaction other than the rhythmic curling of its tail against the plywood. Jesse peered down at the can again and snorted. "Honestly, I don't even know why I bought this crap in the first place…" It rolled again within his palm and he squinted to read the ingredients. "…It's quite inferior to the real thing…full of sodium and sugar… congealed slop'n'noodles… that's what they ought to call it… Unfortunately, I don't have the venison, beans, or patience to make something proper. Sadly, you're just gonna have to deal."

In fact… As his gaze wandered among the stack before him, he wallowed, *I can't remember the last time I'd cooked anything… after all, what's even the point?* His fingers absently tightened around the can.

"My wife, Sophie, used to say… 'You should become a chef!' – she'd always say that… You should do this! You should do that… Well, I don't know… Maybe, I should have just listened, right?" His nostrils flared with amusement and he slowly pulled himself to standing. "Well, turns out; I should have done a lot of things…"

After procuring a can opener, he slammed the drawer shut. "Maybe if I made more money, I could have helped her too..."

He dumped the contents into a small, unwashed bowl and pushed it before the animal. "And maybe if I made more, we could have come here together, a lot sooner... Or at least lived somewhere a little nicer. Enjoy."

Jesse stood back and watched on as the animal neared its nose toward the bowl for a tentative sniff.

God, I'm such a jackass...standing here, talking to a stupid cat of all things. ...I am losing it, aren't I?

Several times, and as though the food were snapping at it, the cat's head slotted backward until it withdrew into a tight hunch.

"What?" Jesse sneered. "You want me to pick out the tomato chunks or something? Maybe microwave it for you? Hm? Well, too bad. In case you haven't noticed, I ain't got one..."

It did not take long for him to submit to Bigfoot's vacant staring. Rolling his eyes, he reached in with his fingertips and fished out one of the bigger pieces of processed beef. Waving it beneath the animal's nose, he huffed, "C'mon. Just try it… It's not that far off from cat food. Trust me."

Against a defiant swat, the morsel escaped his fingers and made a small stain on the floor. With his hand still suspended in the shape of a pinch, Jesse grimaced and craned his head, "Dude, c'mon…"

Purring, the cat stood, stretched, and hopped onto the floor. After a moment of awkwardly staring back into its expectant gaze, Jesse blinked, grabbed the bowl, and gently set it down before the cat's paws. He backed away again and observed. There, Bigfoot thoughtfully stared into the sludge, before rising, sniffing, and finally taking several, big bites.

"Oh, so is that the trick then?" Jesse's brow perked. "You're awfully particular..."

He tucked his hands firmly beneath his armpits and surveyed the cramped van around them. Rubbing the sticking residue into flaking strings between his fingertips, he privately realized, *Yeah... In guess you're going to need some kind of setup, aren't you?*

January 14, 2012
Newport

"Whoops!"

The cashier's hand was quick to catch the slender can as it tipped against the end of the sliding belt. Rotating it in her palm, she curiously inspected its label with a squint, but after a thoughtful puff, she smirked, and slipped it into the bag alongside a small parcel of catnip.

"Can I see your I.D.?"

Jesse smirked, not quite anticipating the question due to his untamed appearance. Still, he kept any comments to himself as he unraveled the beaten wallet and held it up for her to see.

"Oh..." She gestured coyly, pinching her fingers. "Can you take it out, please?"

This time, he couldn't restrain a scrunching expression, though he wordlessly wrestled the thin card free. He sighed impatiently as the woman's eyes dutifully snapped back and forth between the picture on the card and his present face. His mouth twitched into a forced smile, in some attempt to emulate the photograph, though his attention habitually drifted. Against a chaos of colors, his eyes were drawn to her well-worn name tag, loosely dangling from a blue lanyard. Though its typeface was starkly legible, it was crowded by a collection of small, peeling stickers. They depicted cartoon oranges in various costumes, those which he recognized as belonging to bulk tangerines. ROSIE.

The sudden presence of his license slotting between his thumb and finger startled him back into the present. Looking down at the card and its once-familiar portrait, he couldn't help but feel mocked by that crooked, insipid smile he used to often wear.

"So, you're from Idaho, huh?"

Forcing another smile, he merely nodded and stuffed the card back into its sleeve.

"That's cool!" Oblivious or apathetic to his sullen expression, she went on excitedly, "I used to live there, too. Actually, well my folks are still there… ALL the way up in Couer d'Alene. You ever been?" Lips pursing, his head hardly shook.

"Oh really? Yeah, I guess that's kinda a-ways away from everywhere, isn't it?"

"Yeah, a little bit," he flatly agreed and inhaled. "I--"

"The drive back always su-ucks… You know, now--" the cashier chuckled and nimbly punched his birth date onto the small screen. "- people are always telling me that they're jealous that I get to live here out on the coast. When really, I'm actually kind of jealous, 'coz like… they're the ones that get to be on vacation, right? Like, yeah, I'm on the coast and all, but I'm also always here in this stinky ol' store," she gestured widely toward her bleak surroundings. "Go figure, right? Plus, they're usually not here to see the winters, you know, when the weather is totally the worst…"

His eyes widened.

"Are you on vacation?"

Vacation… Jesse's brow lifted. He wasn't sure why in this moment he was compelled to be so honest, "No. I'm not on vacation."
"You're not?" The cashier perked curiously. "How long have you been here? I don't think I've ever seen you before."

He shook his head slowly. Tracking the movements of her hands as she scanned the cans of cat food, he mumbled lowly, "Not very long... Last year, my wife died, and my landlord evicted me so he could turn the place into a short-term rental... so," he inhaled, "I blew most of the insurance money on this crappy, old van, and... just figured I'd explore the coast... I don't know."

"Oh..." She furrowed awkwardly. "Geez, well... I'm sorry to hear that."

"It is what it is." Though he voiced this sentiment steadily, he could feel a sting worming its way around his eyes. Forcibly blinking, he turned his chin the other way.

Jesus, why now? ... He aimlessly scanned the stacks of candy on the nearby shelf. *I didn't ask for this.*

Upon her sudden arrival, he watched as an old woman began stacking various plants onto the belt beside him. When she registered his blatant staring, her eyes narrowed, and she set down the divider with some force.

"Well, you're not alone, I guess," the cashier sighed. "I couldn't stand to be home anymore after my sister committed suicide. Really kind of did a number on the family, you know? I just couldn't stay there anymore."

Jesse's attention snapped back onto the young employee's face, although he wasn't quite sure what to offer beyond a dumb expression.

"Huh, that's funny..." Her smile, once persistent, began to falter at its corners, but after a small moment of absent staring, it began to bloom once again and she proudly proclaimed, "Well, look at me! That's the first time I've been able to say that without tearing up... Ha!"

He watched her eyes excitedly dart across the features of his face as though he would somehow share in this overly personal revelation.

"How about that? ..." Her gaze turned down and she chewed thoughtfully on the corner of her lip. Self-awareness returning, she exhaled in something resembling a laugh and rolled her eyes.

"Well, anyway…" Snatching the receipt from the printer, she offered it to him, "--you just have a nice day today, okay? Just remember; one day at a time. That's what my therapist says anyway. It only gets better from here!"

Challenging was the infectiousness of her smile, especially as it spread in competition with his own. His eyes turned down and wordlessly, he crumpled the paper away, before moving to collect the heavy bags. It wasn't until he was about to pass through the exit that he stopped and realized, *Through all that, I wasn't even paying attention… How much did that come out to be anyway?*

Fumbling the crumpled receipt out of his pocket again, he tipped his head and took in the total.

That's expensive… Running through the numbers again, he grimaced and determined, *I guess I'm going to have to figure something out pretty soon here…*

Anxiously, he rubbed the paper between his fingers. *… What am I going to do? …*

One day at a time…

He smirked upon the sentiment reemerging in his thoughts, and upon realizing that it had even arrived on his face, he stopped all at once and swiveled his head with thought. He squinted, hardly seeming to register the impatient push of a stranger's shoulder bouncing off of his own. Arriving at some sort of determination, he turned around and made his way back toward the busy register.

It only gets better from here…

March 7, 2012
Newport - South Beach Jetty

How about that? I got a job.

Bewildered, Jesse could only peer into his reflection as it warped within the murky screen of his battered, old phone. His head swiveled as he recounted the conversation.

They really must be hard up... I... genuinely didn't think it would be that easy to find one, let alone even just hear back from anyone...

His gaze separated from the device to instead take in his surroundings. Most impressive was the bridge above him, bursting forth from the fog to sprawl long above the wide, choppy bay. So commanding it appeared that he couldn't help but wonder if it was built upon the back of more ambitious ideals. After all, this dreary town, resembling a miniature from here, struggled to grow around its mighty heels. As a formation of pelicans swept past, his eyes chose to follow them instead, all the way down the length of the crumbling jetty. Not unlike the bridge, the dueling walls of rock began to vanish into the very mists now spitting their salts upon his face. Flat was the sky and water as they bled into one, but the horizon this afternoon felt clean, like a canvas awaiting more. Gradually, the shape of a ship began to break through, with swarms of seagulls curling all around it.

One day at a time. The woman's voice sounded in his mind for another time, and he couldn't help but begin to smile. Pushing himself from the van's dirtied hood, he inhaled deeply and rounded his way toward the door. *Things seem to be going well with that cashier too.*

He smirked.

Life is strange like that, I guess...

He gripped the handle and yanked open the door.

'You should be a chef!' Amused by the irony of his new situation, he snorted. *Yeah, well… I wonder what you would think… You would be surprised, at the very least. And I… I think you would have been happy that I didn't end up alone, either… I remember as you held my hand, you swore you didn't want that…*

As though to confirm this feeling, his eyes naturally sought out the cat. However, the scene that greeted him upon his entrance caused him to freeze in place. Playfully twirling, Bigfoot pawed and gnawed at the feather stuffing once belonging to the old, satin pillow.

Jesse's lip quivered to match the restless shifting of his eyes as he struggled to process the scene. Though emotions of grief, anger, and despair all clashed for dominance within his swelling chest, his voice could only emerge as an impotent whimper as he bleated, "What have you done?"

March 14, 2012
Newport Historic Bayfront

The humid stink of brine and fish lingered heavily in the air within the confines of this old, tiny bar. From the stool on which she was perched, Rosie tucked her chin against her shoulder and scoured their environment curiously. Despite failing to recognize any of these faces, she could somehow sense that they must have often haunted this place. Upon her eyes eventually circling back onto Jesse's, she squinted, smiled, and confessed, "You know, in all the time I've lived in Newport, I've never actually been in here before."

Though he could have said the same, Jesse kept the confession to himself and weakly smirked. Swiveling the base of the pint between his fingertips, he merely inquired, "Is that so?"

Again, her eyes craned behind them. After taking in the crowded tables for another time, she chuckled and insisted, "No way… it's always looked too scary." More flirtatiously, she added, "Plus, I've never had anyone to go with before…"

As the silence waned, she faced forward again so that she could lean to peek over the bar. "I wonder though... do they have any lemon? I forgot to ask." Glancing at Jesse, she gently nudged him with her elbow and mewled, "Can you ask?"

"What?" His face scrunched indignantly. "No, c'mon."

She sulked and pouted into her drink. The seconds waxed on, but upon observing the persistent fullness of his glass, she commented, "You seem grouchy lately."

He laughed stiffly, and she watched his eyes shift indecisively. Rather than respond, he lifted his glass to silence whatever thoughts he beheld behind a long, slow sip.

"I mean..." Her face twisted awkwardly. "... It's fine and all. It's not like I was really expecting you to ask... It just... would have been nice."

He rolled his eyes and with a thump, the glass found its way back onto the counter. Sucking the foam from his lip, he huffed, "It's not that."

"Oh..." Rosie's eyes fluttered and widened. "okay then."

She turned away from him and anchored her head into her palm. From there, he stared at the back of her head, where he couldn't help but admire the subtle hints of silver daylight refracting off the bends of her hair. He didn't need to see her face to read her disappointment, and coaxed by guilt, he bluntly confessed, "I'm getting rid of the cat."

She lurched in such a way that Jesse thought she would leap from the stool, and though he expected her to have some sort of outburst, her eyes somehow flashed with something even louder. "...You mean BIGFOOT?"

He thought to explain himself but couldn't quite work up the nerve. Instead, he pointed his attention at his drink and took down another, more generous swig. In his peripheral, he could only perceive the scrunching of her face as something of disgust. Yet, the more he burrowed into this decision, the more his face warped with the throes of resentment.

"... I don't understand..."

Though the commotion of their surroundings attempted to swallow her small voice whole, it burst against his ear in fullness. Stubbornly, he pretended as though he hadn't heard her.

Her chin returned to the perch of her palm, but this time, she leered at him directly. As time passed, he had hoped she would have turned away again, that the conversation would move on, and or that maybe someone would even come to offer her a drink, but instead, and of course, she began to pry away.

"That cat saved your life, you know."

Though her persistence was unsurprising, the suggestion had certainly caught him off guard. He chuckled.

"Don't laugh," her face scrunched into an uglier expression. "What's the matter with you?"

Really? His brow lifted high, though he coveted his thoughts. *You want to sit here and listen to me talk about my dead wife and what her possessions meant to me? What she had meant to me? Is that what you want to hear today?*

His head turned, and he returned her stare as though she could somehow hear this inner monologue. After searching her features, he determined, *... But, I'm such an asshole, right? To you, to her, to everyone... Even to the god damned cat.* His eyes rolled and pointed down again. *What the hell am I even doing here anyway?* The salty air, still foreign in this form, was quick to fill his lungs.

Rosie's head wagged impatiently, and as he rubbed his face into his hand and turned away, she scooted toward him, ducking to chase his eluding gaze.

"You know, if it weren't for that cat, we never would have met... Don't you ever think about that?"

"That's not true," he smirked. "I would have come in to buy beer eventually."

"Yeah," she huffed. "--like I'm just going to talk to some jerk who's only coming in to buy cheap beer all the time. With all that other stuff, I just thought you at least had a heart was all."

By the time he looked at her, she was already turned the other way again. He smiled softly, losing himself in the nuances of her hair again. With the way it folded, he couldn't place why it would make him think of that trash bag again, but it did. Thoughts wandering, he asked stupidly, "Well, do *you* want a cat then?"

She remained motionless as though he hadn't spoken at all, and conceding to the brewing silence, he turned his eyes back onto his drink.

"... Do you really think that's what she would have wanted for you?"

Her tone was uncharacteristically cutting, almost belonging to someone else as she went on, "For you to be all alone? ... Or is that just what *you* want?"

His brow creased, and somberly, he stared into the murky beer as though it would somehow answer this question for him. *Is it? ... I don't think so...*

More soft this time, she concluded, "Well, Jesse... I just don't think that's who you are... It can't be."

March 18, 2012
Newport

Jesse tore his eyes away from the wrinkled grocery bag beholding the remains of the old, musty pillow. Instead, he looked impatiently onto the cracking screen of his small, outdated phone and inhaled tersely upon watching a new minute turn over again.

They should be here any second…

He tensed against the sudden and familiar sensation of something soft winding in circles around his legs. Unable to bring himself to look at the cat, he seethed bitterly, and kicked, "You get the hell away from me!"

Bigfoot yowled impatiently, before nimbly jumping onto the counter. Rhythmic as always, the animal's tail drummed softly and silently upon its surface. As this movement perpetuated in the corner of his eye, he could not help but feel as though the creature were somehow mocking him. He turned his head, but upon locking gazes with the cat, and despite his withering glare, it merely tipped its chin downward, before aimlessly pointing its gaze about the room in pursuit of something invisible.

You don't care at all, do you?

He hardly had time to consider the fallacies of such a thought before the muffled chugging of an engine materialized in the neighboring parking space. Upon its quieting, he glanced out the window, before checking the screen of his phone again.

That must be them.

The woman was already standing there by the time he tugged open the door. Smiling briefly, she gestured to usher her daughter to a safe place along her side. "C'mere, baby. It's time to meet 'Kitty'."

The young child bashfully peeked at Jesse before hiding her smile in the folds of her mother's jacket.
"Hey there." The woman affectionately stroked her daughter's frizzy locks. "I'm Madelyn. We're here about your ad for the cat?" Her eyes took on a more dubious shape upon scouring the van for another time.

"Yeah..." For a reason he couldn't quite find, Jesse's gaze separated from their faces to latch onto nothing in particular.

I guess Rosie was kind of right... If I just get rid of Bigfoot, then what do I honestly have left? Again, and oblivious to the narrowing stare of the woman, he was haunted by Rosie's words. *"That cat saved your life, you know!"*

This time, and upon coming to again, his focus sharpened around the image of the cat's inquisitive stare. From the countertop, it calmly and rhythmically unfurled its tail, with a small sliver of sun bending bright against the bell of its collar.

Do you really think that's what she would have wanted for you? ... For you to be all alone?

Decisively, he exhaled and swiveled his attention back onto the woman.

I'm a fool...

"Uh..." Already anticipating how stupid he might sound, he cracked a smile but tried to bury it as he announced, "You know... I... I already gave it away."

The woman's face twisted. "You're kidding me. We spoke this morning..."

His lips pursed and his expression evolved into something even more awkward. His head shook, and though his mouth parted, he couldn't manage to summon a better explanation beyond a dim-witted shrug.
"I drove all the way up here from Waldport, because you said you were going to give us this cat. And now, you're telling me that you already gave it away? Is this some kind of joke?"

His teeth grit, and again, he shrugged. "I'm... sorry?"

Peeling her hand from her hip, the woman gestured furiously, "Well then, why don't you explain to my daughter why she isn't getting her kitty today. On her birthday, no less." Beneath her breath, she added, "Unbelievable..."

Jesse reluctantly returned the child's increasingly bleary stare. So bizarre and confrontational the situation felt that he couldn't help but restrain another laugh. However and somehow finding it in himself to appreciate her visible disappointment, he answered, "I'm sorry, it's just... It turns out, I think that... somebody needed her more..."

March 4, 2012
Newport

This feels... Strange...

Jesse watched the onions shrivel and darken amid the golden oil of the well-worn pan.

To be doing something that I... like?

He smirked.

Switching off the heat, Jesse looked up to take in the kitchen for another time. It certainly wasn't the glamorous setting that he had envisioned in past daydreams, especially with the stacks of canned clams in the corner and piling dishes waiting in the sink, but to even be there was satisfying anyway.

"Welp!" The hoarse sound of his co-worker's voice cut its way into his trance. Grinning triumphantly, Billy crumpled the ticket with his fist and threw it into the brimming trash can.
"Yeah! Kobe ain't got nothin!"

Brow lifting, Jesse asked, "Uh... Shouldn't we hang on to that?" Waving his hand dismissively, Billy grunted, "Nah. That guy's a regular. He never complains 'bout nothin'. It's actually kind of impressive."

Swiveling to face their other co-worker, sweating dutifully over the fryer, Billy gestured wildly until he captured the man's attention. With the joining of their gazes, Billy pointed between himself and Jesse, before clumsily declaring "Ti-mando un descan-to?"

The fry cook smiled in a way that Jesse could recognize as forced, but either oblivious or apathetic, Billy beckoned, "C'mon. I need a smoke."

The cook's smile became more genuine as Jesse shrugged and offered an apologetic glance, but with that, he followed Billy through the open door, leading out toward the hidden, locked-down dumpsters. Taking in the moss that clung to the steel, Jesse could not help but think of that homeless man for a reason he couldn't quite place.

Wonder what that guy's up to now…

Cigarette already underway, Billy squinted through the plume of smoke unfurling from his nostrils. After a moment of thoughtful staring, he gestured loosely toward the van, parked along the fence, and asked, "Say, how long are you planning on living in this thing, anyway?"

Though Jesse snorted with amusement, the smile didn't quite reach his eyes. Staring at the pavement, he could only manage a short shrug before grumbling, "It's just impossible to find a place, man."

Now mirroring Jesse's posture, Billy chuckled and dipped his head. "Yeah…" He fiddled with the filter of the cigarette, before agreeing, "You don't gotta tell me about it… Shit, I remember when I first came out here, I had to stay in a yurt down at South Beach for a couple of weeks, before totally lucking out with my current landlord." Triumphantly, he added, "Met a guy that knew a guy."

"A yurt," Jesse's smile was more genuine this time. "Fancy."

With a huff, Billy's brow bounced before he pulled from the cigarette again. Exhaling, he went on, "Genuinely thought I was going to have to start sleeping in the Walmart parking lot or something in my old beater, but it all worked out… Anyway, the whole point of me

28

bringing this up was that my stupid, annoying neighbor and her even dumber kids *finally* moved out, and my landlord loves me, so I don't know. If you're looking to get into a place, I could probably put in a good word for you. Pay it forward, right? You're a good guy--"

Jesse frowned dubiously. "I got the cat, though."

"Yeah, I know," Billy nodded. "He doesn't mind pets. He knows how hard it is out there..."

Peering into the window of the van, Billy raised his arm and wiggled his fingers toward the conspicuous shadow of the animal observing them from behind the thin curtain. He smirked upon the sudden emergence of its paw, batting defensively against the glass.

"Hey, c'mon, don't tease her," Jesse grumbled.

Billy snickered, but following the natural waning of his smile, he insisted, "I'm serious, though..."

As though to prove it, he started to rummage through his pocket for his phone. "Here... I'll even give you his number, right now..."

Jesse's face scrunched upon watching Billy's thumb cut paths through the thin layer of grease that coated the device's screen. As though becoming aware of it himself, Billy took a moment to wipe it against his apron, before presenting its face to Jesse. "Just see what he says... I know he's eager to fill the place, but he's always complaining about the 'riff-raff', you know?" He chuckled, and added, "Just tell him you're a friend of mine. And more importantly, that you have a job."

Jesse stared at the number skeptically, before unfurling his arms to accept the device. Itching his cheek nervously, he privately conceded, *This van bullshit is starting to take its toll on my back... That and the cold...*

"Yeah... okay. I'll think about it."

"Attaboy." Billy grinned eagerly and slapped Jesse on the back. Upon the meeting of their eyes, he gleefully declared, "Well, Jesse! I look forward to calling you 'neighbor'."

April 9, 2012
Newport

"Man, traffic is just awful right now!" Rosie's complaints were as instantaneous as her emergence from the tiny vehicle, which quaked upon the slamming of her door. Turning around to face the highway from which she had just arrived, she gestured violently, "These tourists, with their big ol' campers-- Apparently they need all that room to pack all their stupid shit, but then they forget to pack their fuckin' brains."

His brow lifted, seeming to pull another smile up with it. "All this coming from a fellow Idahoan? ... I mean, what's really the difference between us and those tourists at the end of the day?"

Her face bunched with offense, but reading her expression, he playfully pressed, "Well? Then tell me; how long does one have to be here until they finally lose their T-Card?"

Rosie's head dipped, and she snorted. "You're gross."

"Maybe..." He chortled. "Either way, I'm glad you made it here in one piece."

"Yeah..." Her eyes widened and rolled. "Barely."

She took a moment to survey the tiny, cracked parking lot, surrounded by what seemed to be an equally modest apartment complex. She squinted, and upon turning around on her heel, she was faced with the chain link fence sharing a lawn with an empty restaurant in the neighboring lot.

"Well, the view isn't as good," Jesse joked. "--but, at least I get to wake up to the smell of freshly baked bread every day."

As her gaze settled back into his, she began to smile, mirroring the one still lingering upon his face. After a moment of simply absorbing each other, she inhaled deep, and stretched out her arms into a loose gesture, something resembling a wide, relaxed shrug.

"Alright, I'm ready!" Her arms fell back onto her hips with a thump and a bounce. "Let's see it then; Jesse's grand, new palace!"

He scoffed, though he agreed, "... I guess compared to the van, it is sort of a palace, even if it is just a studio."

Amused, Rosie's face bunched and she followed close as he withdrew beneath the shelter of the staircase to open an old, mossy door. It cracked open just a little, revealing at first a huge, empty closet although the wall in which it sat did bend into the suggestion of space beyond what she could see. Her eyes widened with curiosity, but before she could move forward, the presence of something soft weaved in circles around her ankles.

"God damn it--"

"Well, well, if it isn't ol' Bigfoot," Rosie, appearing unbothered, giggled and swiveled to keep eyes upon the cat. As it stopped once just to yowl, she folded clumsily to stroke its arching back. "Hello to you, too, pretty girl!"

Bigfoot purred affably.

"Get over here, you little butt-head," Jesse growled between his teeth, finally managing to scoop up the cat. Like liquid, its body stretched long against his grip, only to condense back into a more recognizable shape as he hugged the animal to his chest. Seeming pleased and comfortable with its new vantage point, it glanced about curiously, before purring and curling up for comfort.

Jesse and Rosie briefly touched knuckles as they joined in scratching the animal's small head, but upon the annoyed flickering of its ears, she receded her hand to instead reach into her shoulder bag.

"You on lunch?" Jesse watched as she fumbled through her belongings.

She nodded wordlessly, but just as Jesse predicted, Rosie produced a wrinkled clementine.

"Boy, scurvy's just got nothing on you though, does it?"

He couldn't help but laugh at her perplexed expression. However, registering that he must have been teasing her, her face scrunched defensively. Religiously, she peeled the small label from its rind. Her chin tucked steeply into her collar as she carefully flipped over her name tag, and somehow finding a space, she proudly added the sticker. "I don't have this one yet... Heh, he's got a hat on, too. Look at 'im..."

"You got quite the collection going on there..." Playfully, he flicked at the plastic, prompting her to swat.

Then, squinting thoughtfully, she asked, "You think it's worth anything?"

"No."

They shared a short laugh before Rosie swiveled on her heel to take in the parking lot for a final time. Cramming a segment of the orange into her mouth, she chewed once, before pointing, "By the way-- Any takers on that old, ugly thing yet? The sign's gone..."

Jesse's gaze followed, and knowingly landed upon the van, tucked snug in the outermost corner of the parking lot.
Expectantly, Rosie looked at him, only to become reinfected by the long, smug smile now expanding across the length of his face. Swatting at his arm, she pried, "Well? Did you?! Is this finally it?"

He nodded, though his head seemed to slot into the posture of a bashful dip. Wordlessly and for another time, he smoothed his hand down the length of the cat's pulsating back.

"Hmm." She swayed thoughtfully. "The end of an era."

For a reason he couldn't quite place, the sentiment caused his smile to recede into something more resistant. After a moment of reflection, his brow bent, and he agreed, "Yeah... I suppose it is."

Rosie hopped on both feet to better face him. Arms expanding, she cheered, "Well, aren't you excited?!"

His face mutated with confusion, but with the return of a genuine smirk, he inquired, "About what?"

Her eyes rolled as though it should have been obvious. Playfully spinning, she gestured toward the sky and declared, "The future! D'uh!"

February 11, 2019
Lincoln City

Well this is it... With some effort, Rosie grimaced and lowered herself onto her knees. Retrieving the box cutter from between her lips, she pushed up the blade and sliced through the tape that fastened the old cardboard together. *This is the last one...*

The plastic of an old, blue grocery bag greeted her first as she peeled back the flaps of the box. Curiously tipping her head, she untied it, only to find remnants of what looked to be torn cloth and bent, greasy feathers.

What the hell is all this?
Her brow knit as she combed her fingers through the material. *Why would we just have a bag of trash like this? ... But, come to think of it, it actually kind of looks like a...*

Out loud, she realized, "Oh... Jesse."

Upon holding the handfuls of fabric and feathers between her hands, Rosie couldn't fight back a somber smile.

But isn't it kind of funny though? ... The way you end up in the places you least suspect? I always thought my first house would be in Couer D'Alene. Or maybe even in Spokane if things were really looking up... and maybe that would have been the case if you hadn't done all those drugs, Angie...

Shoulders slacking, she paused to stare at the ceiling before absorbing her surroundings for another time. With the presence of all the clutter, the space was starting to resemble a place of comfort, somewhere people could truly live. Eventually, her eyes came to a stop on the single, framed photograph hanging slightly crooked on the wall. There, she admired the image of her infant's fresh face in the center of a soft vignette, and her smile began to grow even wider.

Loss does take us to the strangest places, doesn't it? Somehow... things blossom from what used to feel so... meaningless at first. ... Well I'm glad to be here.

Her attention switched back to the remains of the tattered, moldy pillowcase. Rubbing a feather gently between her fingers, she mused, *... Either way, maybe I can make something nice with this... Like a quilt or something. I don't know. I'll figure something out... I may never have known you and... well, you probably wouldn't care for me very much, considering...* She chuckled softly. *But, I think you should have a place here too. Don't worry...* She returned the material to its place very gently. *We'll take good care of Jesse.*

She flinched against the feeling of something soft colliding at her back before collapsing.
"Oh... Hi, you," she smiled, running her hand down the length of the cat's rigid back. It arched weakly, enough so that she could feel the bumps of its spine punctuating the crevices of her aging palm.

She sighed, conceding, "You seem to grow thinner by the day anymore, don't you?"

Her eyes lifted to take in the nearby bowl of food on the floor, still untouched from some time that morning. The cat heaved, but audibly this time. Although it followed a while of seemingly vacant staring, Rosie did arrive at that grim realization. Her hand adhered to the shape of the cat's ribs, and there, she could feel the suggestion of fizzing from somewhere within its lungs.

"...Bigfoot. … Is that why you've been hiding so much lately?"

With slow movements, she reached into her shirt to retrieve her cell phone from her bra. Pressing her knuckles to her lips, she merely stared into its screen for another moment, before somehow finding the courage to navigate through its various menus. The dial tone chimed only a couple of times until the line snapped with the pause of reception.

A familiar voice was quick to greet her ear, "Hey, love!"

Her voice caught in her throat as she hesitated.

"No! No, no, no! What're you doing?!" Jesse's voice briefly became distant, followed by the clattering of metal and a small, panicked voice she didn't quite recognize. "You are going to burn down the whole damn truck if you put that in there--" Returning to the receiver, he apologized, "Sorry, I'm just training this new kid that Billy hired... Funny, I used to live in a van, and now I work in one. Ain't that some shit?" He chuckled. "Anyway... What's up, Buttercup?"

Rosie's chest rose as she drew in another breath. "Jesse... It's about Bigfoot..." Following the silence, she beckoned, "I think you need to come home right now..."

February 11, 2019
Rocky Creek Viewpoint – Depoe Bay

Sunlight dappled the shoreline in iridescent rays, and each layer of the sky was a solid, clean, and pleasant shade of blue. Against the cool breezes, the trees swayed in a carefree manner, in such an uncanny way that Jesse had to think of Rosie, even if only briefly. His mouth cracked a grateful smile, but it was short-lived and breaking.

Reluctantly, his eyes separated from the scenery to take in the presence beside him. There, in the passenger's seat of the little, green

Buick, Bigfoot rested within the confines of a blanket, nearly looking peaceful, though Jesse knew better.

"Well... Here we are again..." Jesse's hand easily overlapped the head of the cat. His fingers curled against her fur, but they were delicate in their intrusion. "You remember this place, don't you? ... It's certainly been a while... Maybe a little less trash, this time?"

He wasn't sure why he stared at the back of her head for so long. It was as though she would somehow give him a response. In the silence that stubbornly followed, he watched her draw difficult and shallow breaths, and with the sunlight bleeding in through her naked ears, he could see all the little veins dutifully transferring the functions of life, even if it was fleeting.

Gingerly, he wrapped his hands around the bundle, but when he lifted her, she felt weightless. For a moment, he thought back onto the trash bag, before forcefully pushing that memory from his brain, however fond it had become by now.

I can't think of that now...

For a few more lingering and precious seconds, he cradled Bigfoot to his chest, before finding it in himself to open up the door. The air was cool and fresh as it enveloped them both, and it followed after them, as though wishing to guide them to a place at the cliff's grassy edge.

I don't know if I deserved it, or if it was a part of something much greater that I'll never come to understand, but... you were with me. And, you stayed with me until I made it to where I needed to be. His hand overlapped the cat's head once more, but this time, her ears did not perk back into place. Affectionately playing with the one anyway, he wondered, *But, did I help you too? ... Are you now where you need to be? And where are you going now? I wonder...*

Raising his head, he watched the atmosphere turn slowly around the world. Though the rain seemed to be collecting into heavy clouds in the distance, they drifted peacefully toward the horizon to deliver their fury elsewhere.

Will you say 'Hi' to Sophie for me? And ,maybe Angie, too? Let her know I'm taking good care of Rosie…

His chin lowered, and through the film of tears blurring the surface of his eyes, he watched the cat's fur separate and bristle in the wind.

Things really won't be the same without you, I know, but…

"Thank you, Bigfoot." His arms tightened around the blanket, though it had since become still within his grip. Though he knew that she had left now, it didn't stop him from whispering, "Thank you, for saving me from myself…"

Skinny Boy

By L.W. Smolen

"Skinny Boy's constipated again," she said. "It's been three days! What did you let him eat?"

"I never let him eat anything but dog food!" he snapped back. "You're the one always has to stop and talk and doesn't pay attention and he gobbles the seaweed."

She'd just come back in out of the rain. She started toweling her black dog off. Her wet hair hung miserably down around her face.

"There you are, baby," she crooned to her ten-year-old dog, filling his water dish. "Want some water, baby? There you go, sweetie."

She truly pandered to Skinny Boy; seldom to her husband. Her husband was jealous, but somehow, the deep softness of her voice as she coaxed dripping Skinny Boy got straight to his heart as it always had, back when she talked to him that way. Some days, he resented Skinny Boy bitterly. Some days, he loved that stupid Poodle. Some days, he could really see why she did. Some days, he hated himself for hating a stupid dog.

Countless times, before she got up in the morning, out in the cold, dark garage, he'd climbed into his worn-out rain gear and stood out on the beach in the buffeting weather waiting for Skinny Boy to – git 'er done. Countless times, waiting on Skinny Boy, he'd gripped the corners of an end of a poop bag, held the taught edge up to his mouth, and blown and blown, trying to get the opening to separate, but found out he was blowing on the wrong end of the bag. And when Skinny Boy'd finally assumed the position and done it – why, the bizarre sense of success was palpable! He could walk Skinny Boy home and go in and report with a smile that, "Skinny Boy did it!" and their day was off and running.

But today, it was all about bitter resentment and rain and he knew it would dribble cold down the back of his neck, rain gear or not.

"I'm gonna take him out again," he told her. "Give him another try."

"I don't see what you can do. I'm just going to have to take him up to Newport to the Vet today for sure."

But, see, it was worse than doggy constipation – a lot worse; it was their Anniversary and he hadn't been able to think of a single thing to get her – not even a decent card; they were all too corny or sappy or made a joke out of twenty-nine years of voluntary monogamy with a woman who still seemed to him to be some sort of gypsy – a magical shape-changer.

"Don't worry, hon," he managed to say. "I'll just step on him out there. It'll come out of him like toothpaste."

TWENTY-NINE YEARS! She'd had to live with this type of humor. Right now, she was only pretty sure her husband was joking.

But an hour later it was still raining cats and dogs and blowing a full gale and with a hopeless thud of the back door, he and Skinny Boy headed out to produce. Normally, Skinny Boy towed the holder of the other end of his leash. But not today. Today, Skinny Boy hurt.

"Our twenty-ninth," he thought to himself with a deepening sense of doom.

Suddenly, an angry realization hit him. Half a mile from home, clear the hell down by the boat ramp, he stopped dead. Both he and Skinny Boy stopped still in a lake-like puddle. Had he even organized himself enough to bring along a poop bag? In nervous irritation, cussing himself, he started frantically searching his six pockets. Too many pockets. Just then, less than a mile out over the ocean, simultaneously – Flash! Slam! BOOM! Lightning, then thunder struck. Skinny Boy froze still. He shrank. His head and tail drooped. Watching Skinny Boy tremble in abject terror, he knew it was over – the hope that doggie constipation wasn't permanent. He knew, too, suddenly –

39

too suddenly, that he was never going back – never going home, never could stand to face her empty-handed on the Anniversary of their wedding.

"Do you think we should get married?" he'd asked her more than thirty years ago. It hadn't really been a question. They had, though – gotten married. They figured they added up to something. They didn't know what. It was all a dream that blotted out the World. They were different, but it didn't matter. They loved each other.

So, hopeless, he and Skinny Boy kept walking numbly through the rain – just monotonously covering distance, heading for high ground, mindlessly ascending. He started up Eckman Creek Road. He knew it just diminished to a narrow, overgrown log track that eventually led miles back up into a snow-line-high area called Desolation Saddle.

In the western woods, clear-cuts grow back with a jungly vengeance. The road was a groove through the black trees. He passed a ghostly, abandoned RV. Somebody had pulled a big section of the aluminum skin off. Shredded pink insulation hung in soggy clumps. Two flat tires. He knew he was looking at a dead dream. He got more depressed. Two hours? Three passed? Who could tell? No more thunder. No more lightning, just the half-overgrown, weedy log road tunneling through the silent, dripping forest, winding away into a chilling Infinite.

It struck him, though, that he could let Skinny Boy off leash!

It should have made a difference. Normally, off-leash, Skinny Boy immediately realized his freedom and took off running in big arcs, then circled back, waiting for a stick to be thrown or – gittin' 'er done. This time, though, Skinny Boy just stood still and stared at the wet brush sagging under the soggy weight of Winter.

All of it steady elevation gain, five, six miles, he guessed he and Skinny Boy followed the empty old road. He guessed they were up now about twelve hundred feet. Under his rain gear, he was sweating. He started to worry about hypothermia. They weren't that far from the saddle. He guessed, too, that they weren't alone as it felt. And it was getting dark. Predators would be moving around now - lurking behind the impenetrable gloom of the black forest – looking for mortality to eat.

With a visceral squirm, he remembered he was bare-handed. Quickly, he glanced around in the murk. He shrugged. He saw nothing to worry about. Then he remembered that's how it is in the jungle of the western woods; they see you first. He reminded himself thankfully that the last rifle season was over for the year. He wouldn't die that way. No. Not accidentally blown away. He could turn and head back down right now, but he could also be getting stalked right now. Worst, Skinny Boy hadn't – gotten 'er done.

Just then, without a sound, it was over.

Out of thin air, right in his face, they were blocking the road – the Elk. The huge shapes of the herd of at least a dozen bigger-than-horses Roosevelt Elk plugged the road, towering unpredictably in their lanky power. Ten yards away, a giant bull Elk with a rack wide as the back end of a pick-up truck shook his head; ready to defend two immediately visible calves, it lowered its huge rack ominously.

GAME ON! Skinny Boy exploded into Super-Retro-Puppy! He didn't bark. Speeding, he circled and leaped crazily around one of the calves. It froze still. The giant Bull puffed and tried to wheel to face Skinny Boy, but couldn't keep up.

GAME OVER was just as abrupt. Quite naturally as could be, Skinny Boy's back end caught right up close to his front end. He assumed the position. He started. Seizing their queue, the Elk all stepped silently back behind the dark curtain of their western woods.

By the time Skinny Boy was finished, the road was as empty and silent as before.

In disbelief, habitually fumbling for his poop bag, he walked over and gawked down at what Skinny Boy had accomplished. It was trophy-sized. Coulda easily mistaken it for bear scat.

41

By this time in my life, I'm somewhat of an experienced writer, but there is just no way to describe the stupendous numerosity of the facets of my sense of pride on our twenty-ninth as later, I handed my wife that bag of still warm dog shit.

Sacred Creek Song

By Jill Hagen

Most creeks are special for a variety of reasons. This one is special and unique. It is a protected creek for Pacific Salmon. Rain, snow, and spring-fed, it flows throughout the year. No fishing, no pollution. It is one of the few salmon spawning creeks where the fish return from the ocean and fight their way upstream to their hatching place to lay their eggs for the next dwindling life cycle. This activity happens twice a year. It is rare to still see the natural cycle and balance of Mother Earth.

In the late summer, when the water level is low and running clear, you may find crawdads and immature insects under some of the various-sized, perfectly smooth, round rocks that fill the creek bed. Some of the smooth stones may be the size of Volkswagens. Many stones are head-sized. Most are fist-sized as the pebbles and sand wash farther downstream toward the Pacific a few miles away. The rocks are ancient and sacred.

During the hot summer days, the creek makes a very soothing background sound like the muffled murmurs you felt in your mother's womb. The babble of the stream, just like the pumping and flow of your mother's blood has a calming effect, mesmerizing, almost hypnotic.

When the fall and winter rains of the Pacific Northwest return and the weather pattern experiences collisions and upheavals, we get the unsettled periods of RAIN, wind, RAIN, hail, RAIN. Pineapple express.

The many miles of steep forested hills surrounding the canyon and valley become quickly overwhelmed with the moisture. The creek swells with the rain from the hillside run-off. Heavy rain results in a flash flood and the raging river flows dangerously fast. The sounds of the creek quickly go from babbling to roaring, the appearance from clear to muddy.

The creek has changed into a creative force. It now has the strength to move even large rocks and dislodge trees. People fear change but nature does not.

During the time of increased water, you can hear the trees breaking, hear the rumble, see the rapids churn. Then an unusual sound begins. MMMMMMMMM..plunk...plunk. Like warming up vocal cords, or testing the drums, or tuning musical instruments.

MMMMMMMMMMM...louder, more percussion sounds, like notes. The creek has begun to warm up her voice to speak. Her song is emerging. She is starting to sing.

There are more notes in the air, the sounds more complex and louder, with greater range.

Think of the water and the process in musical terms. Smaller rocks make higher-pitched sounds. Ting, ting. The ting level is higher, and more frequent, like a muffled snare drum, or background music.

Increasingly heavier rocks are easily moved about the raging, churning water. They make deeper sounds as they are rolled along. Each collision of the smashing rocks produced tones like a beat from a fancy drum set, mini explosions. As the rocks and boulders kissed each other, they demanded attention. Various notes are created with each size of rocks moving about. A full, complete, unique, very loud song.

Not only were there sounds, a song, coming from the creek but all the intense movement within the water seemed to send out energized waves. A person can see the raging water, can hear the percussion song but some things are not seen through the eyes nor heard by the ears, not physically obvious. All this activity in the rapid water creates an intense series of vibrations like atoms, ions, and molecules in constant motion.

For me, it caused a sense of optimism, energized cells, overwhelming emotions, thoughts to ponder, and a greater awareness. Life out of chaos.

As I listened all night long to the creek singing, the experience resulted in several changes in my life. Less obvious, less tangible. There are few words that can describe a night of creek singing, maybe because it was more than words could describe. Sounds, images, thoughts, feelings, and heightened awareness. A sense of clarity in the orchestra of the music and vibrating energy. Life out of chaos.

An elder who has lived by the creek for over half a century reported that the creek may sing once or twice a year, but this recent event was far louder and longer than remembered past. All night long the creek sang its songs. The intensity of the event evoked and created vibrations and positive energy waves that permeated the hillsides for miles around. It was nature, Mother Earth, in her glory, singing, creating but humble about her ability to make drastic changes.

Shortly after the event, salmon returned on their quest. As the water receded, the position of the rocks in the stream bed was visually altered and the stream banks were changed. The creek sang louder and longer this time, maybe because people heard her voice, her message, and truly were affected and energized by the experience. The song she sang is now muted.

As I have become connected to Mother Earth, I can hear animals talk about the coming earthquake, hear trees cry, see and feel bolts of energy, sense my daughter's life with a dragonfly, and now I heard the sacred creek sing. A gift, truly appreciated. Like with previous tests and gifts, with each awareness on this journey, another door opens.

Sacred? Foretelling? Sharing secrets and wisdom? The creek sings and uniquely shares what each person can hear and feel. I felt I knew more about the history surrounding the creek.

I knew that many Native tribes used to gather with great appreciation for the creek. She provided fish, drew the elk and deer to her waters. The creek helped each tribe sustain their winter food supplies. There were many meetings that ended with love matches. The energy of love, of passion, and hope, fills the creek valley.

Truly a special sacred Northwest coastal ancient creek.

Whittling

By Jill Hagen

Whittling is an old hobby but new to me. For the first time in a long time, years, my world felt at peace.

Picture this.

I was sitting on an outdoor folding chair on the covered porch. My two pups were taking naps on their big pillows. It was nearing sunset on a warm mid-summer day. There was a gentle breeze, just enough to cause the wind chimes to ask for attention. They offered a heavenly sound.

The sound of the Sacred Creek below the house was in the background. It babbled with a gentle heartbeat. Birds sang in the trees, seemingly grateful and thankful for a good day of life.

The task was whittling. I was working on a few Sacred Creek Wands by smoothing out the handles and shafts of the wood. It was important to sense and be open to how each wand would evolve and be enhanced. Glass, copper, carving. It was like meditation to touch each wand of wood.

My mind was at peace.

The thoughts of medical issues, paying bills, doing dishes, laundry, or mowing the lawn didn't intrude. The always-present sadness about losing my husband, my daughter, my parents, or numerous friends and animals didn't intrude.

Was it the touch of the wood? Was it the repetitive motion of whittling off a small sliver of wood? The wands had already been dipped into the creek. Maybe the wands were already working to heal and to bring a new positive energy.

My body was at peace.

I felt the world was momentarily at peace.

Did you ever get a sense you are where you are supposed to be?
I now understand why many older folks carve, whittle, and touch wood. The wands had each been dipped into the Sacred Creek and will each be smudged. Because the wands have been enhanced with a bit of copper the energy and emotion will be swished with greater connections.

Anyone using the wands needs to keep positive energy in mind. I have been reminded, recently, that what is sent out can return. What goes around comes around. Or is it what comes around goes around? I never get sayings or jokes correct.

I also never win lotteries, or win at slot machines, and have never caught the flower bouquet at the wedding toss.

I recently received a letter from a credit card company. It stated that an account in question had no transactions in three years. My husband, who died three years ago had several dealings with the credit card company. The letter stated if the credit card company was not contacted, the account would be placed in an abandoned file.

Shortly after my husband died, a friend helped me understand my financial status. There was a question about an account with the credit card company that was left unanswered. And soon forgotten. After I received the letter, I called and discovered there was a small savings account.

Maybe my energies were changing.

I could've traveled around the world with my husband, the scientist. He went to Europe, Mexico, Canada, Australia, and the Far East to address the state of the local water. I often said I would rather stay at home with my smelly dogs rather than travel. It feels to me that the world is made of one big onion, everyone, everywhere cooks with onions. I am very allergic to onions.

In the last 6 months, for some reason, I have been thinking of a trip to Iceland. I discussed a tour with several friends and made a decision that I would go and save for the trip.

After investigating the issue with the credit card company, I knew Doug was sending me to Iceland. Doug had a savings account in both our names. It was just enough to make the Iceland trip possible. Was the energy in my life changing? Time will tell. The coastal energy, the sacred creek energy, the energy of whittling the wands, and the touch of copper; was it all coming together to make changes?

The Guest Book

By Savannah Gardiner

Welcome to the cottage. We, like you, visited this cottage on a trip to the coast and fell in love. My heart broke as we left to return home. Soon after our trip, the cottage was listed for sale and we jumped on the opportunity to buy the cottage. While it is our home most of the year, we are grateful that during the late summer, we are able to share it with families like yours. If you feel inclined, we'd love for you to sign our guest book. It's always been one of my favorite parts of visiting a vacation home. Reading the experiences of people that were once in the place I'm staying. Help yourself to a cup of tea and enjoy the unmatched beauty of a sunset from the porch swing. We sincerely hope you enjoy your stay at the cottage. ♡ **Sue & Kevin**

*

This is my first visit to the Oregon Coast since I was a kid. My family used to stay in Florence at an old motel. Our trips were filled with sandcastles and kites and too much sugar around a beach bonfire. It has always been the place I let my mind retreat to when I need to find my happy place. My new husband, Miller, had never visited the coast, so when he let me choose where we would spend our honeymoon, it was a no-brainer for me. The coast for sure! We found the cottage online and nothing I looked at even compared to the charm I felt through the pictures. I knew that the couch would be deep enough to fall into, but I had no idea that it would feel like falling into a big fluffy feather bed. Sue, you were right, the sunsets are just absolute perfection. The only thing that competes is sitting on the porch swing and watching the fog and mist move in before the sun makes its debut each morning with a cup of that strawberry elderflower tea. I tried to find it online and can't. Where can I buy it??? It's absolutely to die for! Thank you for sharing your cottage with us. It was the most relaxing week and just the perfect way to kick off our marriage. We will absolutely be back! **-Kensie**

It rained the entire four days I spent here. I wanted a beach getaway, I could have stayed in Portland if I'd known the forecast was going to be completely wrong. Did just about every puzzle in the cupboard. They are all missing at least one piece. Don't even bother with the puzzle of the dogs on bikes, it's missing no less than a dozen pieces. Don't drink tea, so I didn't try that, and it was too rainy to see the sunsets. But the fireplace was nice if you don't mind having to tend to a real fire, it's not just a flip-a-switch gas fireplace. **David**

*

Wow. I used to tell my kids that if they were going to complain, they needed to add something positive "Find the sweet berry in the middle of the sour!". So if David ever returns to the cottage, I challenge him to look for the sweet berry. I visited the cottage in the wake of a pretty devastating divorce. My girlfriends planned a weekend at the coast to heal my soul and the cottage was the perfect place to do this. I've spent every vacation for the last 18 years in chain hotels, somewhere where our points could accumulate to more stuffy chain hotel stays. The cottage was like visiting that eclectic aunt from the movies that we all secretly wished we had. Sue has spent obvious time, energy, and passion decorating the cottage to make it feel like the coziest place on earth.

Jeff, the neighbor was just a peach, he had all the best recommendations in town. The addition of the greenhouse bathroom was something that the pictures clearly didn't do justice. On a particularly stormy afternoon, I was joined by a bottle of wine in the oversized garden tub. The windows overlooking the sea let in enough light that I was able to just sit in the moodiness of it all and let myself grieve and heal. Kensie is right, that elderflower berry tea is warm and cozy while also being light and uplifting.

This was the trip I needed. Thank you Sue and Kevin for sharing your home. **-Nadia**

*

The cottage was lovely. We thoroughly enjoyed our stay. **Sharon**

Thank you to everyone who has shared this last year with us. We've stocked up on the elderflower tea, but for those who want to bring a taste of the cottage home, You are able to purchase it at Coven Cafe in town. I've also replaced the puzzles in the cupboard. Those that were there previously are the ones from when our kids were growing up. I should have known they had pieces missing, so I apologize for that. Enjoy the late summer storms and make yourself at home. ♡ **Sue & Kevin**

*

We're back! The second I got home, I called Sue and booked our first-anniversary trip to the cottage. Miller fell in love with the magic of the coast, just as I expected him to. But this year we're not alone! We welcomed our first son Iverson just twelve weeks ago. Our very own honeymoon baby. Seemed only right to bring him back to see it for himself!

We spent the whole week just walking along the shore with Iverson in the baby Bjorn. The cottage was just as magical as I remember it. I did run into town and grabbed some tea to take home, though I'm sure that it won't taste as good as it does here. I just feel like when I'm here, nothing else matters. Everything is right in the world. Is that just the vacation mindset, or is it normal to feel like that for even people that live in Lincoln City? If that's universal, I may need to give up the conveniences of city life and make the move permanent. Thanks again, we will see you next year, it's already booked! **-Kensie**

*

We came for the beach, stayed for the vibes. **- Girls of Alpha Chi Omega**

*

It rained less this time than last. There's my sweet berry find. I enjoyed the new puzzles and made sure to steal a piece just to drive people crazy. Just kidding, I'm not a dick. Even though reading my entry last year, I can see how that would come across. That being said, Kensie, it was a little harder to go to sleep last night knowing that it's where you conceived your son. I could have gone without knowing that. But congratulations nonetheless. **David**

*

Kensie, we may have similar personalities because I too booked my next trip the moment I returned to the real world. And happy anniversary! I'm celebrating one year of singlehood and am just loving the journey into self-discovery. My therapist gave me a list of homework to do during my visit this year and thankfully there was enough rain to once again enjoy a bottle of wine while watching the storm completely engulf the greenhouse bathroom. Again, Jeff next door is just lovely. We talked for ages on the porch during a particularly torrential downpour. His garden is definitely something worth admiring. His late wife planted it and he does everything he can to care for it.

I brought a bag full of books but didn't find quite enough time to consume them all. Beauty and distractions all around. Thank you for once again sharing your home with me. **-Nadia**

*

Lovely week at our favorite lovely cottage. **Sharon**

*

We are so grateful for return visitors and it looks like we will be sharing with some of you again this year. So welcome. New changes this year include the handmade soap in the greenhouse spa. It's all locally made and you can find it at the Saturday market down at Salishan. We also arranged to have fresh flowers delivered each Thursday morning, so if you are staying at the cottage on Thursdays, feel free to bring them in and grab a vase from the hutch in the living room. ♡ **Sue & Kevin**

*

    Sorry David, but there is something in the water here. We celebrated Iverson's birthday this year by welcoming Chauncey, our new baby boy. Born on Iverson's birthday just 39 minutes earlier than Iverson's time of birth. We were hoping to spend the week letting Iverson run all along the beach, but he must be going through a growth spurt because he wanted nothing but to sleep and snuggle on the couch which is something I dream of back home.

    That couch is made out of pure bliss. I honestly don't know how life gets any better than it is at the cottage. And Nadia, if you return, I took your recommendation of trying to chat up Jeff, the neighbor. I don't know if there is more than one Jeff, but Jeff with the big garden was a bit curmudgeonly. I couldn't get even a smirk out of him. Maybe he has a thing for you? We'll be back next year… maybe with a third baby in tow?

    Haha no, there better not be. I'm tired. **-Kensie**

*

    Kensie, I laughed out loud when I read your entry. Jeff certainly has a hard shell. But I must just have the magic to crack through that. I was surprised he remembered me when I first pulled up. We enjoyed dinner at the cottage on my last evening. He even brought fresh veggies from his garden and threw together his Nona's minestrone recipe. I gave up alcohol this year so there was no wine in the tub. But plenty of rain. The new stereo was a welcome surprise. A little Ray LaMontagne with the rain with the smell of the handmade soap and those crafted candles is something I look forward to all year. I'll be back next year and am already counting down the days to the greenhouse tub… and maybe seeing the cute neighbor too. **-Nadia**

*

Jeff the neighbor is my kind of people. He's not curmudgeonly Kensie, he just doesn't naturally have pep through his veins like you do. And that's not a dig at you. You seem to find joy in every part of life and that is to be admired. Some of us just run on a lower frequency. It didn't rain at all this week, so I didn't get a chance to delve into puzzles. I took a fishing charter out and caught a dozen crabs. Too many for me to enjoy by myself. So I too had dinner with Jeff the neighbor. And Nadia, he has a thing for you. He speaks so highly of you, I think he'd trade Sue and Kevin for you. I hope you two exchanged info because I fear he may try to bribe Sue to give him your phone number otherwise. **David**

*

I'm new here. Feels like I need to preface with that since the other guests all seem to have rapport already. Nadia, the neighbor is the cutest little old man. I don't know how old you are, but you should go for it. He's adorable. The greenhouse bathroom is what sold me online, and it did not disappoint. I could live in that bathroom. If you walk just south on the beach, there is a clay deposit on the shore, I harvested clay and crafted some spoons. I found a pottery studio in Newport and had them fired, before glazing them. I'm leaving them here for future enjoyment. The cottage really is magical. **– Lucy**

*

Thankfully Jeff didn't trade us in for a new neighbor this year. So we are still able to share our home with old and new friends. The spoons Lucy made are all in the corner hutch next to the vases. The flowers will continue to be delivered every Thursday. The fire pit in the backyard is yours to enjoy. Thank you all for sharing your memories of our home. Reading our guest book is our favorite part of returning home each fall. ♡ **Sue & Kevin**

*

The cottage was a welcome sight after this last year. We returned home last fall with Iverson still just lethargic and received the news no parent ever wants to hear. Iverson was diagnosed with brain cancer. We are three surgeries and more chemo appointments in than I can even count. This week we just wanted to be present in the place that brings us all nothing but joy, because we desperately needed it.

Miller and I arranged for a sitter so we could enjoy a night out for our anniversary. Tidal Raves in Depoe Bay has the absolute best clam chowder I've ever had. The cottage really is the loveliest place to stay on the coast and is magical in its ability to bring Miller and I close despite the living hell of having a sick child. We will be back next year, with two healthy boys, manifesting this into the universe. Thank you Sue for being so accommodating in our reservation this year. There is nowhere we'd rather stay. Nadia, I look forward to seeing an update on you and neighbor Jeff this summer. Lucy, those spoons have a craftsmanship that deserves to be in high end stores. Please update us on where we can purchase some. I need a set for home. **-Kensie**

*

Well Jeff was disappointed that the visitor after Kensie wasn't a certain Nadia. He did, however, join me on a fishing charter this year.

We went up the Siletz river and caught a 46 pound and 38 pound Chinook Salmon. Jeff knows his way around a smoker. I'll be eating well all winter. I haven't told Jeff that he's the subject of many entries in the cottage guest book, but somehow I don't think he'd be surprised. He seems to know he leaves an impression on people. I know that the charming cottage doesn't exactly fit my style as a single guy in his 40's, but it has grown on me. It beats having to drown out the sounds of people when I have to stay at a normal hotel. I did add a puzzle to the cupboard. It's dogs on surfboards. The puzzles had a little dust, so I might be the only one that does them. But it's the only time of year that I actually do a puzzle. It's meditative and nice. **David**

*

Kensie, I am so sorry to hear about Iverson. I've worked in pediatric oncology for decades, I know it will be a year before you see this, but feel free to reach out to Sue and get my contact info. I'd love to see if there is anything I can do for you all during this time. It's bizarre to think that my first trip to the cottage was four years ago. I arrive at the cottage each September a completely different woman than I was the previous September. I first came here hurting and unsure and trying to find solace in wine and a week of solitary. But I have found myself in the bottom of teacups and submerged under the bubbles beneath the stormy skies of the late summer storms in a greenhouse-converted bathroom. I've healed on the shore behind the cottage, feet sinking into the sand and heart falling into something I wasn't ready for. You were all correct. Neighbor Jeff might have had more than just neighborly friendliness when it came to me.

He reached out when he was in San Francisco and we met up for dinner. Come to find out he had no reason to visit the city, he just didn't want to wait until September to see me. I never visited the cottage intending to find anything but solace. I didn't realize that solace would come in the form of the cute neighbor with a garden dedicated to his late wife. Thank you Sue and Kevin for providing a soft place for me to land and brush myself off. **-Nadia**

*

Kensie, I will gladly send you a set of spoons. I can only hope that they will bring you a smile in an otherwise trying time. Keep in mind that the hardships you are going through are only a season of your life. I have full confidence that next year you will have your two healthy boys running into the waves while you and Miller watch from the sand, wondering how you survived.

This guest book feels like when I had a penpal growing up. I found myself looking forward to reading the entries the whole summer leading up to this trip. The Nadia/ Jeff love story happening in real-time is just an absolute fairytale. I visited with Jeff while I was working with clay on the back patio. He commissioned me to craft and send a set to Nadia as a gift and the honor was too much for me to say no to. Don't forget us when you are sending out wedding invites someday. Again this week at the cottage was exactly the creative break my soul desperately needed. Of course, thank you to our lovely hosts.- **Lucy**

*

I lost my beloved husband Gideon this last spring and the cottage was his favorite place for us to stay. It was a nice weekend remembering him in his favorite place. **Sharon**

*

I never expected when we began renting out our home that we would have a list of regular visitors, nor that Kevin and I would grow to care and even love so many of you just through our brief annual interactions. We want you all to know how deeply we truly appreciate you choosing to stay in the cottage year after year. ♡ **Sue & Kevin**

*

Sue you truly have created a home that feels like home. Which I'm sure is why we all keep returning year after year. Although this year is bittersweet. We lost our sweet Iverson this last spring. His last months were only made possible through Nadia who Sue was kind enough to pass my contact info along to. You all know Nadia as the divorcé who has captured not only our hearts but the heart of the curmudgeonly neighbor Jeff. But I had no idea she is also a world-renowned pediatric oncologist. She arranged for Iverson to be moved to UCSF where she gave him six more good months. No mother should ever have to bury her children, doing so has nearly killed me. If it wasn't for Chauncey, I know I would not be here.

Nadia was there for us through losing Iverson and it's easy to see why Jeff fell completely head over heels for her. Despite the anguish and grief, I'm currently drowning in. It's still hopeful when I'm here at the cottage that life can once again return to the bliss I felt when Miller and I first visited, and again the first time we brought Iverson and spent the entire trip walking the beach, searching for the hidden floats, the third trip when I held my sleepy snuggly boy, blissfully unaware that our world was about to be thrown into tumultuous tides, where we would be unable to resurface the same.

I'm here this year not because I'm chipper and ready for a vacation. I'm here because I still feel Iverson here, on the fluffiest couch in existence. I feel him in the vibrations on the sand when I stand and wish the water would swallow me whole and let me drown for real. I am looking forward to meeting some of you for real later this month for Nadia and Jeff's wedding. **-Kensie**

*

Kensie, I am so sorry for your loss. Thank you for leaving the photo album of your precious family. Looking through photographs of you all here at the cottage it's impossible not to fall in love with not only Iverson but your entire family. I'm grateful that you were able to create lasting memories in a place we've all come to hold dear. Thanks to you all and your words of encouragement, I actually quit my corporate job, making it possible for me to make art my full-time career. **– Lucy**

*

I'm here this year not to just escape my boring job that I've come to resent when I return from the coast. But to celebrate neighbor Jeff who has become my best friend and brother.

I arrived in high spirits and found myself doing something I hadn't done since I was a boy. I cried. I didn't realize how invested I was with your family Kensie until I read your entry and felt my heart drop. If I'm honest, I resented your endless positivity over the years, as it's not something that comes naturally to me. But I don't know how you could have made it through the loss of Iverson without a disposition such as yours. I've called and made a donation to UCSF in honor of Iverson and wish there was more I was able to do. Like you Kensie, I look forward to meeting you next week. **David**

*

It felt wrong to come to the cottage and not write in the guest book. Especially for those staying at the cottage years from now who will no doubt look for the answers as to what transpired between Nadia and neighbor Jeff. I am writing not as a guest this week, but as the guest. Sue and Kevin were gracious enough to agree to host a wedding here at the cottage.

Five years ago I met Jeff who had lost his wife close in time to when my own marriage was ending. We were both trying to find the sweet berry in a patch of sour and were equally doubtful that anything sweet would be found. Jeff wasn't the only sweet berry I found though. I met you all.

Five years of reading only snippets of who you are and filling in the blanks of who I thought you were. Sadly I met Kensie under tragic circumstances, but she's grown to be a cherished friend. I look back to her entries and can't help but let the tears fall for the young bride who was so full of life and optimism. I know she will find her way back, but it will be a journey. David, the man I was sure I would avoid if I found him in a grocery store due to his negative first entry has become my beloved's best friend and in turn a dear dear friend. Sue and Kevin who have been more than just the annual hosts but send us e-mails throughout the years, not only with updates regarding our bookings, but to check in on us and our lives.

And finally, Lucy, who was late to the party, but such a breath of fresh air. My stays on the coast will no longer include baths in the greenhouse unless I can convince cute neighbor Jeff to build one in the garden we will tend together in memory of not only his late wife Melinda but also sweet Iverson, the little boy who stole and shattered my heart in a matter of months. I will always look to my time at the cottage and my penpalship with you all with nothing but love in my heart.

Thank you Sue and Kevin for everything. I look forward to being your seasonal next-door neighbor. **-Nadia**

*

I wasn't invited to the wedding. Not sure why. But the weather this week was beautiful. **Sharon**

*

We don't know how we can top a wedding at the cottage. But we will have space this year for new guests as our long time beloved guest Nadia has given up her annual week at the cottage in exchange for our neighbor Jeff. Love and happiness to all this year. We look forward to reading your updates from your time at the cottage.
♡ **Sue & Kevin**

*

I find myself this year where Nadia was the first year she visited the cottage. Newly single and looking for relief. I can't believe it's taken me 6 years to take her advice of bringing a bottle of wine and some moody music to the greenhouse bathtub, but it is far more healing than I ever gave it credit for.

We sadly lost Chauncey this year to the same cancer that took Iverson. Just as they came into this world, exactly 1 year and 39 minutes apart. I find solace in knowing that they are together. And there is nowhere I feel them more than here at Sue and Kevin's cottage. I would move into the small guest room full time if they ever decide they need a roommate.

For now I will sit, watching the mist roll in, with a mug full of the elderflower strawberry tea that reminds me of my younger self. The me that was full of zest and was sure that the world would have nothing but blessings to give. I will sit with my grief and nostalgia and know that one day, when I return to the earth, my essence will be here, on the grounds of the cottage, running and chasing my boys to the sand, racing to the waters edge and feeling whole once again. **-Kensie**

*

Kensie, I was sorry to hear about not only Chauncey, but you and Miller as well. I am glad that you once again found your way to the cottage as I was worried when we spoke on the phone earlier in the summer that you would eventually decide not to make the trip this year. I am glad you are able to feel your boys here. I will always carry the vision of Chauncey walking down the aisle as the most dapper little ring bearer that ever was. I'm grateful I was able to meet him and fall absolutely in love with him. You may not feel the world blessing you right now. But having those boys, even for the short time you did, will stay with you forever as the greatest time in your life. And as I said on the phone. I will keep my eye out for cute neighbors while at the cottage and send any your way. **-Lucy'**

*

This may be my last summer spent at our beloved cottage. My firm has offered me a position in Edinburgh to open the European branch of my company. This is not news to us Cottage dwellers as our group text is so aptly named, but like Nadia I don't want to leave questions for those that may follow in years to come, taking my coveted week spot at the cottage. May all newcomers become long timers, and find the same camaraderie that we cottage dwellers have. Thank you Sue and Kevin for sharing your home with me for all these summers. **David**

*

Long time no write. As we all know following Sue's passing, Kevin made the decision to move in with his daughter in Ohio. And as you all know, I preemptively made an offer on the cottage, saving Kevin the hassle of needing to put it up for sale.

The cottage for what felt like my entire life was my happy place. It was where I celebrated a new marriage, welcomed my two beautiful boys, and came to feel them in the years after their passing. It is still the place where I feel them the most. I wake up every morning and swear I can still hear the patter of their feet through the hallway.

It doesn't matter that it's been nearly a decade since losing Chauncey. I'm grateful for our ongoing friendship through text all these years later, but it will still never quite live up to the excitement of that last 10 miles of the drive to the cottage, knowing that I would be seeing an update from all of you about your lives. So while I was looking through the last box of Sue and Kevin's I came across our old guest book.

I was the first guest and it only felt fitting to make the final entry in the book. I'm sending this copy of the guestbook so that you all can reminisce with me. On the story of how Nadia and Jeff met and fell in love. How Lucy found her calling as an artist. How David found happiness and moved to Scotland. And how Sharon felt slighted in the fact that she didn't warrant an invitation to the wedding. Please don't be strangers. You know where to find me. I'll be at the cottage.
-**Kensie**

My Name Is John

By Tim O'Brien

My name is John, easy to remember, it's a household word. Folks call me Jersey John, or just Jersey, on account of my accent. I vend fresh roasted peanuts in lower downtown Denver on the streets around Coors Field, the "Home of the Colorado Rockies". The nut thing has been working for ten or twelve years. I work other sporting events: the Broncos - the Rapids, but the Rockies are my bread and butter.

Every week in late September, I drive my Tacoma down to Dothan, Alabama, the "Peanut Capital of the World". Peanut farms stretch for miles around Dothan, east over the Georgia border and South to the Florida Panhandle. My favorite farmer to buy from is Wilbur. His prices are always fair, and he helps me load my truck. He is First Nation Cher-O-Creek. His family has farmed this land since the peanut boom after the Civil War. He always greets me "Hey baseball guy, ready to pitch some nuts?"

At the end of September Dothan has the Peanut Festival. I come for the great prices, but it's a vacation too.

The festivities are at the Peanut Fair Grounds. Work done, soaking wet, and it was still over eighty degrees at eight o'clock; I showered and cranked the A/C. I'm ready to check out the festival. It's a short walk to the fairgrounds, along the way are Dothan's wild and weird peanut sculptures in all kinds of crazy colors and patterns. My favorite is a giant fire hydrant shaped like a peanut beside it is a Dalmatian his paw resting on the hydrant, a big Scooby-Doo grin on his face. They make me smile.

At the Fair, there are craft booths, places to learn the newest trends in farming peanuts, and a carney alley with games of skill and chance. You can win oversized stuffed animals, sports stuff, and silly giant hats. My favorite is the milk bottle toss. It's where I won my lucky

63

jersey. Ten balls and I scored seven. I had my pick of any prize on the wall. Tucked away in the corner at the top, almost in the shadows was a number seventeen Boll Weevils jersey. The Boll Weevils are Dothan's minor league baseball team; they're a farm team for the Atlanta Braves. The carney snarled when he handed me my prize. I grabbed it and slipped it on over the top of my tee.

After the games are all the rides, Tilt-A-Whirl, Teacup, and the Ferris wheel. Like a kid in a candy shop, I tried everything. There was a beauty pageant too, with beautiful women all dressed to the nines. Back in my room, I would imagine riding round and round on the Ferris wheel with any one of them, maybe even getting a kiss. The next morning all packed up I started the long drive back to Denver, cutting north and west skirting all the big towns till I hit I-25.

My friend Kate rents me a corner of her studio. A big warehouse, that shut down back in the 90s. Kate's digs are in the back: The center of the studio is filled with Kate's canvases, oversized abstracts full of swirling colors and designs. My space was in the front. I had a room with a kitchenette and a tiny bath. Next to me was a storage area big enough to store and roast my nuts. When I was roasting the sweet, nutty aroma would fill the whole studio. If Kate was around, she would come to munch a bit, and we would visit.

On game days, I loved taking it to the street. The night before I would roast a batch of nuts, and fill my red wagon with two and five-pound bags till it overflowed. I liked to find a corner between game day parking and the stadium. Situated I would start my mantra:

"Peanuts! Fresh roasted peanuts! Baseball and peanuts!

Get your peanuts! Baseball and fresh-roasted peanuts!

Baseball, baseball! Fresh roasted peanuts!

Get your peanuts!"

Compared to prices in the stadium, mine are fair. I think I gave the people a good deal, but some nights I couldn't sell out. It would happen with the scalpers, too. Sometimes, if I was lucky, I would trade the last of my load for a ticket to the game. Those are the sweetest nights, game day basking in the sun as it slipped behind purple mountains. When the lights came up and I heard the crack of the bat there was no better place to be. The cheers when the good guys scored brought a twinkle to my eye.

March of 2020 the world turned upside down; it shook and shook till we were all pennies on the floor. COVID deaths, uncertainties, the Rockies season canceled. I've always said to myself, "John, put one foot in front of the other." I could no longer see the way forward. I sat, waited, and sat some more. Doom and void: no income, my inventory gathering dust, and worst of all-nothing to do, but my plate wasn't full yet.

Stress ran high in our neighborhood. Crime surged. Kate's friend Zoey's studio was broken into, and her sculptures were smashed. They didn't even rob her. They were destroyed without rhyme or reason. The world was on a razor's edge. No matter which way you fell, you were in the abyss. I'd been living at Kate's studio for seven, maybe eight years. We didn't run into each other much. I would leave the money in her kitchen. When I did see Kate, she always gave me a warm smile, sometimes she would ask, "How's the peanut game, Jersey?" I'd say, "It's crackin." April and May dragged on. The news was all bad. COVID gained and people died. The numbers were staggering-the suffering, the loss. There was no reason to roast. No reason to fill the studio with that warm, nutty aroma. I could still pay my rent, but I wondered for how long.

Late June, the catalpa trees were in bloom. Decked out in delicate orchid-like trumpets with purple veins and yellow spots. There was a tree on every other block and one in our alley where we parked behind the studio. Kate was waiting by her Subaru when I pulled in.

"Jersey, we have to talk," Kate said.

"Okay," I said.

"Can you come down after a bit?" Kate asked.

"Sure, I'll be right down," I said.

"Let's have a glass of wine," Kate said.

My gut said trouble. We had shared a drink once or twice, but never by design. A storm was brewing. I could smell it. We were good, but not really social. Kate's friends treated me like I was a welfare project, and maybe I am. I stowed my shopping and headed across the studio. The big canvases stared at me colors twisting and turning like my stomach-my heart pounding. All our jobs were shot. Mine was dead in the water. Was Kate going to pull the plug? Was there a better, richer tenant waiting in the wings?

Kate had portioned off a part of the warehouse next to her kitchen to make a sitting room. The couch and chair were a purple-gray; like little purple potatoes, warm and shiny. The partition walls are whitewashed and framed in black trim. The art was sparse but whimsical; a windmill-powered airplane, a crazy cat riding a bike, and sculpted turtles stacked six high-at the bottom it said, "All The Way Down". I grabbed the chair holding tight to my seat. Kate came in from the kitchen with two glasses and an oversized bottle of wine.

"You've got your lucky shirt on. It's going to be alright, John" Kate said.

All I could think to say was, "Okay."

Kate said, "John, you know I care about you, but I have to make some changes to take care of me. It's not just the pandemic or the sacking of Zoey's studio. Things are tense. I don't feel safe. I know I can count on you, but our lives beat to different rhythms. Another thing I've had to consider is the skyrocketing value of real estate here in town. If I sell now, I can buy something in the mountains and escape the fear and disease. Next week a realtor is going to start showing the place. I don't know how much longer we will be here, but you can stay till the end. There will probably be some work for you too. I can help you find your way, John."

My brain screamed: homeless, jobless, hopeless. What in the world am I going to do? "Kate, you have always been so good to me. Sharing your home. Treating me with respect and dignity, even if I am just a peanut vendor hawkin' in the street. I want the best for you, but I don't know where to turn," I said. I started to cry a little. I couldn't stop. Kate came over and put her arm around my shoulder.

"John it's going to be all right, and you're not peanuts. You can make a new start," Kate said.

"I don't have a clue," I said.

"Let's take a look at what's out there. We can see what's online. You can go anywhere, a different city, Dothan maybe, or the coast, even another country," Kate said.

I took a couple of deep breaths and a last sob. I said "The ocean, I think. We went once or twice when I was a kid. Do you think I could wind up at the shore?"

Kate said she didn't know but that we could look online tomorrow. Kate poured us another glass of wine. We were both quiet and full of worries. When I looked at Kate's face, I could see she was scared too.

The next afternoon, I headed down to Kate's room. Kate was reborn. Last night's gloom was gone. "Jersey I've got an idea. It will be hard work, but it's a place to land; a job, a room, a new start. Seapacfoods in Newport, Oregon, is hiring for the crab harvest. Work starts at the end of November. You can rent against your first paycheck. Have you heard of Newport? I have some pictures. Want to see?" Kate asked. I sat down at Kate's computer and scrolled through images of Newport. A real, working fishing village, boats all up and down the bay. There was a spectacular bridge over the bay, and a jetty leading out to the ocean.

"Okay but what would they want with me?" I asked.

"It's a big operation, I don't know what you would be doing, but they will find something for you. For now, you can help me get the place ready. There is a lot to do. I'll take out a little rent and pay you the rest," Kate said.

The months flew by. Kate was right, there was plenty to do and lots of junk. Kate got a roll-off and we cleaned the house. Kate's new place was on a hillside outside Morrison. It was smaller, but there was still room for the big canvases. On dry days we hauled them in the truck. We were a sight to see; giant paintings, riots of color, mounted on the back of a truck rolling down crazy Colfax Avenue.

Late October and we were done. The new owners were in the loft. Kate was happy in her new digs, and I was on the road to Newport, Oregon, with a bit of cash in my pocket. Heading out to crack some crab. Excited but scared too. North on 25 and west on 80. Wyoming is long, but so is Miles Davis's "Kind of Blue". I listen to it over and over again. The scrubby hills go on and on. The lush mountains of Utah were easier on my eyes, but the Salt Lake City drivers are insane. Five lanes of bumper-to-bumper traffic. Cars and semis darting in and out near misses and screeching brakes. 84 goes north out of Salt Lake through Idaho and over the border into Oregon.

Portland was tough too. Bridges going everywhere back and forth across the river. I found my way south on the 5. Pulling out of Corvallis, the sun dropped orange stone crashing into the mountains. In Colorado we would call these hills, sometimes steep, but the summits were all less than a thousand feet. The road became narrow and twisty, the forest crowded the road and the temperature dropped. At ten something I checked into the Bay Motel and slept like a little child.

The next morning, coffee in hand, I headed south towards the Yaquina Bay Bridge. I didn't make it over the bridge that morning. I detoured to see a historic lighthouse. Half a block off the 101 the world changed. I felt like I had stepped back in time.

The canopies of massive pine trees stretched across misty gray skies. On the seaward side of the road, scrubby pines sculpted in the shape of the wind pointed the way inland. Flowering bushes studded the park. November, but some still blooming, most a shadow of their full splendor, brown flowered crowns heavy in the wet. Green moss carpeted every tree and bush. It covered the picnic tables, the restrooms, and the historic placards, it was a velvety green blanket that unified everything around me.

The old green-tinted lighthouse stood tall and proud at the top of the hill, beside it was the Coast Guard's Command Center. I could see a head or two bobbing behind the glass.

An ocean gone wild. Not the tourist-filled Jersey shore; umbrellas tip to tip, people elbow to elbow. Pounding surf, a dog walker, a runner, and miles of beach. Seagulls worked the waves and sandpipers ran in and out, darting back and forth with each tidal swell. I felt reborn. The sea and the old growth felt ancient and that made me feel new like anything was possible. I headed back, the road went under the bridge and down to the bay front. Cloud breaks made the morning sun dance on the bay. Columns of light fell from the sky making rippling patches of blue on a green sea.

Down the hill on the bayfront; shops galleries and restaurants getting ready for the day. On the bayside Seapacfoods aquamarine plant covered a city block. A huge banner read: "NEWPORT IS HIRING". I said to myself, "Okay". A bar or two, shops, and a couple more aquamarine Seapacfoods plants and the commercial bayfront ended, and the business of fishing began; rows of fishing vessels and a private marina and I was out of town.

The tide was low: snowy egrets and blue herons worked the tidal flats stumbling here and there on toothpick leg, spearing fish and gobbling them down. Newport turned me upside down but in a good way. No Jersey Shore honky-tonk. No Colorado citified life, peanuts, and the streets: hustle, hustle, hustle. The mountains collide with the ocean, ancient lava flows, and wild rivers all tumbling west. That night I could see the flashing beacon of the lighthouse on Yaquina Head lighting my way.

I was up early the next morning with new job jitters. I parked my rig on the bayfront. Seapacfoods offices are in the last plant on the east end of the bayfront. Steep stairs lead up to the offices. The walls are covered with pictures of fishing vessels old and new. Out the window was a world of ships, all shapes and sizes. I didn't have to wait long before Heriberto showed me into his office. I didn't even have to fill out an application, he did it for me on his computer. I peed in a cup; and waited a few minutes. Heriberto came back and told me, "Report to Pedro at six a.m. tomorrow in the west plant, that's the large blue building furthest down the bayfront."

The next morning was cold and foggy. The offices and lunchroom were at the top of an old rickety staircase. I was issued protective gear, and half an hour later I was down on the line. My job was to haul giant tubs of live crabs from the dock to the line and dump the crabs onto a conveyor belt that delivered the crabs to the butchers. The crabs, cracked and cleaned, went on down to the women who soldier-packed them.

Sometimes when Pedro's assistant Luis ran the show, he would plug me in wherever he was short-staffed. I learned how to soldier pack the crab in a tight set ordering of crab halves to maximize the number of crab parts on each tray. There was even a day when Luis sent me to work in the cooking/freezing room. The trays are stacked in thousand-pound units, two units to a pallet on one side of the room are giant vats where the crab is cooked. On the other side are swirling tubs of sub-zero water that are kept viscous by motion and a very high salt content. Finished pallets go to a giant freezer set at fifty degrees below zero. There they wait to be packed and shipped across the globe.

A day's work could be as much as eighty thousand pounds of crab. Hard work, different from anything I've ever done before, but I felt part of something bigger. At the end of the day, we were ankle-deep in crab guts, the stench locked in our noses, clinging to our clothes. The odor was a sour pungent smell, rotten eggs, and the bay at low tide. The days could be long, ten to twelve hours. We worked seven days a week. The weather could be harsh, with wind and rain beating on the dock. Every night you called in to see if there was a catch for the next morning. If the weather was foul enough that the ships couldn't sail, you might have a day or two reprieve.

70

On days off, I still got up early. Coffee in hand I took the trail by the old lighthouse down to the beach at North Jetty. I walked the wrack line where the ocean drops its debris. I beachcombed my way up to Nye Beach, pockets filled with trophies I had found; seashells, bits of ocean-polished glass, and funny-shaped pieces of driftwood. There is a great bakery in Nye Beach. I like the spinach and parm scones and giant Danishes. Breakfast in hand, I headed up to the highway.

Newport's employment office is on the other side of the 101 just past Olive Street. Cracking crab was okay. The crew was wary of newcomers, but hard work speaks for itself. I had found a spot. There was the smell that I brought home every night. You could scrub and scrub, but it still lingered in your nose.

There was the language thing too. Everyone at Seapac speaks Spanish. I learned to communicate without words but it was kind of lonely.

I was always glad for the down days, but they made me a little nervous. I didn't want to touch my savings. With a little help, I learned to job search at the employment office. I made sure to check on every down day. I didn't find much. There were jobs; restaurant, construction, retail, nursing, and hospitality. Nothing caught my eye. I labored on. Food, hotel bill, a beer or two, I was still saving some money. The pandemic was a lingering ache, a dull pain, nothing that a meal and a good night's sleep couldn't fix.

One day I found a posting for a job, it was part-time. The Garibaldi Seaweed Company was looking for a general maintenance person. The job was cleaning vats, keeping up the yard, doing deliveries, and running errands. I filled out an online application. I didn't have much in the way of references after all those years of doing the peanut thing, but why not try? I gave them Kate's number and talked about my years of working on my own, the pride I take in working hard, and my guiding principles of loyalty and integrity. I had my doubts. Nothing local to add, but I told my tale with honesty and sincerity. It worked. They asked me to come up for an interview the next week. I talked to Pedro the next day. He was cool.

Back in the truck, back on the road, wearing my lucky Boll Weevils jersey. I headed north on the 101. The ocean views were like a rolling painting, waves endlessly plummeting into a picture of rugged beauty. I stopped once after Lincoln City at an ocean overview. At the base of the cliff was a freshwater lake with ducks paddling across, their wake left a white V on the water. There was a nice campground with people visiting. On the sand leading down to the water's edge, a child played with a dog. The two darted back and forth, the child's arms waving in the air. I was glad I had come.

Early, I pulled onto Seventh Street in Garibaldi, with time to look around. I opened the door of the truck and the smell hit me like a sucker punch. Years of fishing hung in the air. It was in my nose and the back of my throat, not foul or rotten, but a sweet fish smell, full of ocean breezes; like a whiff of every fish ever brought to port.

Newport's the only harbor I know; it's an octopus stretching up and down both sides of the bay. Garibaldi is smaller and more intimate. Two or three streets crisscrossed Seventh, with a mix of open and shuttered businesses. There was a new restaurant featuring craft beers, and an old eatery, windows packed with curiosities from the seventies up for sale, old warehouses and grilling and smoking houses with big boiling vats waiting for crab.

Young men hauled carts of fish from the docks. Gnarled old timers sat around jawing and waiting for their catch to be processed. I walked down to the docks; there were two rows of private boats and a row of charters, two with sportsmen boarding, ready for their day at sea.

From the docks, you could see an old three-story smoke stack the last remains of an old mill. There is a new mill too on the north side of the harbor. Hardwood West, a company making plywood.

Interview time. Garibaldi Seaweed wasn't what I expected. Ten or twelve tanks, five feet tall, and maybe fifteen feet across. At both ends of the yard, there were pump houses feeding water this way and that. The whole area was enclosed in a formidable chain link fence. The front fence was covered with info about seaweed benefits and Garibaldi Seaweed marketing.

On pins and needles, I waited. Sophie was on time. We talked. She asked good questions about my skills. How I came to apply and where I wanted to be in five years. At the end of our talk, Sophie asked, "Are you ready to go to work harvesting the bacon of the sea? I said, "Yes, I am." We decided I would start in two weeks. I got the job! I got the job! Walking back to my truck, I was on fire. I felt like I had wings, like a seabird floating over the harbor. Stunned, so many changes, so fast. Where was I going to live? How fast could I learn the job? Would it be enough money? Would I fit in? Driving out of town I stopped at a low-rent motel to inquire about rooms by the month. Yes, I could make this work.

Back in Newport, I started to set my world in order. The next morning, I told Pedro. He wasn't surprised, but he thanked me for giving two weeks' notice. The motel desk agent didn't care the coast is a very transient place. People come and go; everything is in flux. There were some down days in my last two weeks. I spent them at the library reading about seaweed and walking the wrack line.

I learned about the bull kelp forests that line the shore, providing a home and nursery for fish, crabs, and shellfish. The feather boa kelp that rings the forest and how they hold on for years and regrow every season. The coolest algae are the sea palms. They are protected from California all the way up to British Colombia. You need to have a special license to harvest them, and even then, you just trim fronds leaving stipe and holdfast to carry on.

Learning about seaweed changed walking the wrack line. What I saw was no longer a jumble of green stuff. The bull kelp was easy to identify, I came to recognize the boa too. It was more fun like I was looking at old friends.

On my last day in Newport, I came across a perfect Sea Palm. It still clung to the fragment of mussel shells where it had lived. It was army green, all its fronds intact but coated in a fine layer of sand. I don't think sea palms on the wrack line are protected. I took out my knife and cut a handful of fronds away from the stipe. I stuffed them in the pouch of my hoodie. When I got home, I rinsed them and chopped them up. I tried some raw. They were sweet almost and smacked of the ocean. I added the rest to the chowder I was having for dinner.

That night I dreamed I was an ancient fisherman. I lived with my beautiful bride Cylla on a sun-drenched beach. On market day in our village, no one could touch our catch, cool, fresh, eyes sparkling and the smell of the sea on a breezy day. My secret was seaweed. I wrapped my fish in seaweed. I used the whips of the bull kelp to bind each fish and gave each a dip back in the sea.

I landed a good catch and spread it out on the wet sand. There was Bull kelp, but none of my other usual wraps. Instead, the beach was littered with little sea palms. They were clustered in groups of twos and threes. No worries, they were wet and green I secured them to my catch with the bull kelp. Home, and market ready. We dined at the hearthside. Tea and kisses, it was a sweet night.

The next morning, I went to gather my catch. My eyes popped out of my head. It was impossible, the fish were alive, flipping and flopping, their eyes darting here and there. How could this be? I cut a handful of fronds from the sea palms and popped them in my mouth. I chewed and swallowed. I took a deep breath and it hit me. Strong magic pulsed in my gut, and the blood in my veins ran cold. My legs became one, my feet formed the tip of a powerful tail. A dorsal fin rose from my back and webs filled the space between my arms and body. I dove for the waves. I snaked my way down to the surf and into the water. Safe, I tried out my new tail. It was strong and powerful, a snap of my tail and I raced over the waves.

Cylla came looking for me, but all she found was the reborn fish. Panicked, she ran to the water's edge calling my name, "John, oh John – where are you, John?"

I swam back to shore and called back, "Cylla I'm here. I ate some sea palms, and they turned me into a merman with a tail and fins." She saw me and fell to her knees, crying out, "What will become of us?" I longed to go to her, take her in my arms, and tell her everything would be all right, but I couldn't. I had become one with the sea.

In our village there was a story of a powerful sorceress said to live on an island not far from our shores. She was the subject of market day gossip and fodder for children's tales. "If you don't behave, the witch will come and turn you into a crab." Maybe the sorceress could help. I promised Cylla I would try to find her and plead our case. Two snaps of my tail and I was gone.

The sorceress was waiting for me in a cove on her island. She wore a regal purple cloak, and behind her was a lone wolf. Its eye fixed on me, ears cocked for a murmur from its master's voice. How she knew I would be there I cannot say. I told her my story and of the great love that Cylla and I shared. I implored her to help us find a way to be together. She promised her help and gave me a potion corked in a bottle. She said, "Cylla can join you in the sea, and become a mermaid. In exchange, the two of you must promise to spread sea palms everywhere you go.

I thanked her and promised, "We will carry the sea palm everywhere our journeys take us."

I made my way back to our coastline. I found Cylla sitting on the prow of my beached boat. She had been crying, but when she saw me she ran into the waves. I handed her the potion and she drank it down. I saw the look of surprise as the magic struck her. Her legs became one with a tail like mine. She toppled into the water with a splash. She sprouted a fin, and webs joined her body and arms. She flapped her tail and swam a circle around me. She swam back to me with a silly crooked grin on her face. We kissed a wet, wild kiss. We didn't need to say a word. We were together. We swim the wild blue, our love remains true, and we honor the sorceress, spreading sea palms in our wake.

I awoke. What a dream. It was moving day, a mighty flip of my tail and I was on my way.

I love my new life. I wander the bay and the ocean bay split. I've been here in Garibaldi for a month. I'm learning how to take care of the tanks. I think I fit in. I work early mornings at the mill. I clean the bathroom and lunchroom. Between the two jobs, I'm okay.

I'm ready to get out of this motel. I have some housing leads. I think I may have met my Mermaid. There is a woman I see at the mill, she's about my age. She always gives me a big smile and a little wave. I smile back, but we haven't talked. Tonight, I washed my lucky number seventeen Boll Weevil's jersey, and tomorrow, I'm going to talk to her. I know what I'm going to say, "Hi! My name is John, it's a household word. Easy to remember."

Acknowledgements:
Josie Iselin, 'The Curious World of Seaweed'
Journal of Applied Phycology 'Seaweed in Mythology, Folklore, Poetry, and Life'
Madeline Miller, 'Circe'
My favorite reader, and son, Shannon Farrell

Rose in Fairyland

By Leah Shrifter

There once lived a girl named Rose who was determined to get to Fairyland. Rose had golden-yellow hair that reached down to her slender waist, bright eyes that were as deep blue as sapphires, a pert button nose, and (sigh) ruby rosebud lips. She also had big, pointed ears, which is how she knew she was part fairy and needed to get home to Fairyland, where she belonged.

Once she found the entrance, she believed she would follow the winding path through a sunlit enchanted forest where butterflies, birds, and the tiniest of the fairies would fly alongside her. At every bend in the road she would meet a new magical being, like the Unicorn, the Mud Lady, and the Thorny Needle-y StickerMan. Finally, she would come to the castle of the beautiful Fairy Queen who would welcome her home. Rose wasn't sure about what came next, but perhaps the handsome Elf Prince would be waiting there for her, and they would be married.

But first she had to find the entrance to the Fairyland Forest. Rose knew in her heart exactly what it looked like: Low trees extended their branches like eager arms to each other, grasping and intertwining above the trodden path as if holding hands in an arch so the wind could not blow them apart. Once and then twice she saw the forest entrance far away. The third time she found it, right in front of her. She skipped under the leafy arch and there she was…

Oh, not really. She had found many such arbor archways, and there was never any forest leading to Fairyland. Usually, the wind blew in off the ocean through the hardy, stalwart trees at the edge of the beach. And the girl's name was not Rose.

It was Bessie, and she was no longer a girl. She was a woman with frizzy brown hair streaked with gray (not gold) and brown skin the color of coffee with cream. The only gold glints were flecks in her light-brown eyes. She worked every day as a checker at Walmart, in a town along the Oregon coast. However, just like Rose, Bessie had large, pointed ears. She still believed in fairies, but she wasn't sure what they looked like and she didn't believe she would ever find them (or a handsome elf prince). She never talked to her family and friends about the fairies, because she knew they would be afraid she was crazy, or at least way too peculiar.

Bessie found it was not so hard to be a peculiar person, since living in the United States of America was becoming more insane these last years. Anyway, no one could tell by looking at her. She just made sure she walked under every archway she encountered where the trees locked their branches like lovers' arms against the wind. She hoped one day she would walk through the forest entrance and find her way home, no matter what her true name was.

Bessie wasn't really crazy—no more than the next person. But perhaps she was more stubborn, or truer to her own heart. I know this, because today she found her way into the Fairyland forest and her steps along the path wrote the words of this story.

Now I may be a little confused, but I think the rest of us might be the inhabitants of Fairyland. After all, no one really knows everyone who lives there, just as no one in our world knows everyone who lives here. Perhaps if I walked into the blue house across town, I would encounter the Fairy Queen herself.

Or the Thorny Needle-y StickerMan.

The Seagull

By Linoa Linette

When are you going to--

The small text on his dimly lit cellphone vanished with a click against the press of a flat and wide button. Tucking in its stubby antenna and peering into its plastic, narrow screen, Glenn felt somewhat mesmerized by his distorted reflection. In abstract ripples, the impression of his features bent and broke into something refreshingly unrecognizable. Following a short smirk, he determined:

No.
Not now.
Not anymore...

With a snap, the device folded shut beneath his clamping, pallid fingers. For a moment, he even thought to hurl it overboard and into the water, though he resisted this amusing impulse, and instead tucked it snug into his breast pocket. With a soft thump, his hand returned to the curve of his boat's aluminum steering wheel.

...
No... Nope.
I'm not going to do anything...

Against an incoming brace of salted wind, Glenn looked back and watched the Yaquina Bay gradually condense toward a singular point with the expanding distance.

Farewell...

He turned forward again and instead peered through the speckled windshield.

I'm going to keep going... until I can't see it anymore.

Dense, pungent fog poured from the crannies of the forested knolls at either side of the unraveling channel, gluttonously swallowing the fractured beaches, the aging lighthouse, and the contorting, windswept pines. Cruising between the jetties and just before they broke away into the sea, he caught a brief glimpse of a large white van, parked crookedly amid a gravel patch surrounded by beach grass. Against the vehicle's side leaned a visibly bedraggled man, absently itching at his bearded cheek, with his nose pointed permanently onto the screen of what must have been his phone.

Glenn scoffed.

Surrounded by all of this natural wonderment and people still can't separate themselves from what's really not all that important...

Completely erased by now were the ships of the South Beach Marina from which he had remembered disembarking, and fading were the buildings once staggering the bubbling hillsides just beyond the Historic Bayfront. The only structure that seemed to stand against this devouring force was the massive, Deco-styled bridge. However, as the seconds lapsed and his boat barreled toward the horizon, this view also began to gradually succumb to the thickening inversions.

Whatever.
I'm going to keep going... until I can't hear them anymore, either...
Not a soul will be able to reach me...

The deep foghorn of a ship bellowed somewhere in the distance as though to personally protest his reckless and selfish impulses. Head swiveling, he searched the horizon for its source, though the expanse ahead yielded nothing but shattering waves. All he found was flat, milky skies, sporadically freckled with the flocking of seagulls and blocked in by the long, bending surface of the mercury-colored sea.

No, I don't care anymore...
Be damned with anyone else...
I'll be free... just like Dad...

Whatever they want to think about it…
Yeah, there's no arguing that he is free.

Moisture spread from his nostrils upon a stiff exhale.

I'll get lost out here. I don't mind…
Even if I end up missing, just like Dad…
I'll go so far out that even I can't see a thing…
…Yeah.
No one will be able to find me…
… and that…
Well, that will just be… perfect…

This feeble ship, small and modest compared to others, was pushed around easily by the resistant, incoming waves. Still, it cut forth so faithfully and persistently that he mused it was somehow fueled by a motivation similar to his own. The helm was cold and slick by now, but it was persuaded easily by even the smallest suggestions, and through his hands, he could almost feel the boat's determination to hone into those places unknown.

They sped past one of NOAA's buoys, and the distinct scream of an angry osprey clashed sharply against Glenn's ear. Intrigued, he turned his attention toward the sound, and in that direction, it surprised him to see the inversion break away just enough to reveal to him the spectral impression of another boat. As its form solidified upon breaking through the fog, Glenn could see that it was equally small in stature. There, it was bobbing leisurely as it returned toward the confines of the bay. Though he couldn't quite place why he was so compelled to do so, he cut the power to his engine, and curiously tracked the other vessel as it crept up close to the waggling buoy.

The wind plucked at the loose and broken twigs from the bulky nest wrapped snugly around the top of the beacon. It was a decoration he found to be reminiscent of a crown or even a fur skin cap. Surrounding the buoy's red and white laddered pillar, sea lions, rocked to sleep by the rhythmic passing of the waves, lazed in piles on the limited space of its round base. Held hostage by the possessive whims of the ocean's diverse and quirky fauna, Glenn briefly questioned the efficacy of such a structure.

Even from that distance, and as the neighboring boat circled the buoy, he could hear the faint impressions of insipid laughter. Yet, the wind kept bending the noise into something weird and discordant.

Ah! Haaaa! Ha!

The sound cloyed at his senses in an uncomfortable way that he couldn't quite identify. Following a roll, his eyes switched away, avoiding the sight of what he presumed to be tourists now stretching their arms long to force their phones into the space of the easily agitated beasts.

Idiots...

As he once more pushed forward on the throttle, the boat lurched hard to fight against the indignant push of an unusually tall wave. As the furious, high-pitched hollering of the osprey receded into nothing behind him, he couldn't help but dwell on that strange, amorphous feeling. Slowly, it sauntered its way into the forefront of his mind like a coy, familiar, but unwelcomed friend.

And yet... I can't shake the idea that I've somehow lived these moments before...
Yeah... that boat. It looked familiar...
But...

Compelled by this lingering notion, he glanced over his shoulder again, but by now the only evidence of the bay's existence remained the murky, celadon silhouette of the massive arch sprouting from the center of the Yaquina Bay Bridge.

It wasn't until he was surrounded by a nebulous void, both in sight and sound as they pertained to life, that he would switch off the engine for what he hoped to be a long time. With a triumphant smile, he absorbed the moment and began to covet the tranquility of this fragile, but newfound solitude. In the absence of the engine's influence, large waves lifted and dropped the boat with audible slaps and splashes, treating it as though it were just a toy in the ocean's covetous grip. He chuckled.

This would make Daisy so sick...

In response to this realization, his smile naturally receded into a sullen purse, and he began to chew on the inside of his lip instead.

Following another swollen crest and with a thump, the one brittle, rusted crab trap he possessed slid sideways across the deck where it then wedged itself in the space beneath the rail. Though the scratches it created in the lacquer of the boards would have normally sent him into a fury, all he could summon at this moment was a swelling sense of apathy. Twisting in his seat and reclining, he sighed and merely stared at the dilapidated cage. Against the breeze, the duct tape rattling from its flaking rims grew speckled with the fine spray of the sea, and now and again, it seemed to swivel and jostle in its place, as though threatening to free itself and cast its own body into the sea.

Go...

Telepathically, he tried to coax the trap overboard.

C'mon... If that's what you want, then just do it...
Get out of here...
Go...

His eyes grew narrow and he stood up. Ducking beneath the doorway, he emerged onto the narrow deck to loom over the teetering crab pot. Here, the winds were tumultuous as they washed over his bare face in frigid currents, but so immersed he was in his thoughts that their hollering was somehow reduced to impotent bleatings.

I wasn't going to use you for anything, anyway...
You useless thing...

Momentarily, his gaze began to separate from reality, with this thought repeating itself and taking on the shape of a familiar voice. Feeling a pang of anger, his teeth clenched, but following an exhale, he determined instead, *Don't think of that...*

Balancing his boot on the rim of the cage, he sneered and began to crush it, before angrily kicking it the rest of the way past the rails. It collided loudly with the water, and from above, he wordlessly watched until it disappeared into the depths, though this didn't take very long.

Good riddance...

He stepped back and with a thump, he collapsed onto the small bench just behind his knees. Though he turned his head to look at the rod rack beside him, it still required another internal battle before he could register their presence enough to reach for his usual pole. His fingers coiled around the dense, foam grip, and though he pulled it free from its slot with ease, he couldn't help but survey the other rods and think back on those trips that he hadn't taken alone. Somber and dull was the shade of his eyes as he now stared at a small, pink rod in particular. With another long sigh that was followed by a weak shaking of his head, he instead switched his focus onto the one laid patiently across his lap and in his hands.

They're all better off without me anyway...

Intrusive and insidious were these thoughts as they crept their way back into corners of his mind. With his thumbnail, he absently began to pick away at the material peeling from the grip of the rod butt.

No...

He grimaced and shut his eyes tight against a shedding mist.

Enough...
Just stop it...
...
Everyone got their way, after all? Didn't they?

In the two feet of line extending between the swivel and heavy, lead weight, he began to fasten an additional stretch of line that ended with a sizable hook. Inadvertently pricking his finger, he cussed beneath his breath and stopped to inspect the tiny bleeding point.

Smearing it between his digits and becoming absent again, he mulled, *Yeah... I'm never coming back.*

Looking up and across the choppy waters, he lowered his hand and exhaled wearily.

Truthfully, I would just be fine to stay out here... and fish forever...
Just like Dad...

Returning to his task, he pushed the barb of the hook through the rubbery spine of the paddle-tailed bait. Staring back into its flat, painted eye, he smirked wryly.

After all... it's not like the ocean's going to judge me for my choices...
It can't care... It can't think...
It can't even see me...
So, who better to spend my time with now...

With a groan, he arose from the bench and crossed the short distance to the railing to meet the sea. There, he leaned against the bar and dropped the clunky rig into the water. It took a while for the reel to unravel far enough to start knocking upon the ocean floor, and while he waited, he pensively watched the waves lap with an awkward tempo at the silly, sun-bleached title progressively fading from the hull of the boat.

Maybe it's time for a new name, too...

New name, new beginnings...

Eventually, he felt the weight topple and roll against the valleys far below, and patiently, he began to jig the line in a slow and lazy rhythm.

No more yellow eyes or sculpin, please...
Just give me a big ol' lingcod... or even a halibut...
Whatever it is...
Just give me something that I can keep, for once...

Though it felt repetitive, with the weight constantly bouncing off the sea floor, he began to attain a purer sense of peace for the first time since he had begun the voyage. His eyes tracked an incoming forest of kelp that materialized on the brink of the fog. It lingered for only a few minutes, before floating on and away toward some other place into the mists, and possibly beyond his imagination.

I would bet right now... Ted and Daisy are looking for agates
down at Beverly...

His mouth curled into a weak smirk.

Ted sure does try, but... of course, Daisy is always finding
everything...
She's sharp like that...
She takes after me...

The tip of the rod started to twitch and soon after, the line straightened to cut forth across the water's surface. He squinted, surmising pretty quickly based on its fight that whatever it was couldn't have been anything special. Still, he began to reel, but upon seeing the flashes of orange circling their way up toward the surface, he grimaced with disappointment.

"Damn it," he cussed, further scowling as he lifted the rockfish out of the water and over the railing.

On the deck, it landed with a wet, hollow thump, and as it gasped before his feet, he couldn't help but feel as though it were an increasingly pitiful sight. Its eyes, huge and clouded in this form, bulged wildly from the barotrauma incurred by its journey to this side of the Earth. While he expected that it would begin to flail, it did not, and kneeling to retrieve it, he murmured, "Well, thanks for making this easy at least..."

From the rack, he selected another pole and propped it against the railing. Steadying the belly of the fish in one palm, he retrieved the small, black descender from the depths of his opposite pocket with the other. Carefully, he closed the clamps onto the creature's bottom lip, giving it a small wag to confirm it was properly fastened. With some effort, he then attached the descender to the line, all the while privately chastising himself for not having it prepared for such an occasion in the first place. He couldn't reason why, but after accomplishing the construction of this contraption, he took another moment to morbidly behold this unfortunate catch. Unsettling and corpse-like was the state of its face, further repulsive with its enlarged gut protruding from its mouth and pressing firm against the curl of the clamp as though it might burst. However, as though to remind him that it was still alive, its amber frill began to rise and its gills expanded wide to let out another agonizing, tortured gasp.

"Alright, alright... Let's get you home then..."

Leaning over the railing, and to the best of his limited ability, he lowered the rockfish back into the water. Though he expected that it might leap back to life, it did not. Instead, and like the crab pot, he watched on as the fish twirled lifelessly into the deep, inhaling shadows of the awaiting kelp forests.

Well... Not sure what you see in the place, but...
Good luck down there...
...
Quite the traumatic lesson... but, I hope that maybe you've learned something useful today...
...

Who knows? But, maybe after this, you can go on to live a long, and happy fish life, whatever that entails...

Glenn smirked at the absurdity of these thoughts and took a spot on the bench again. Finally inspecting the condition of his line, his smile receded and he blinked hard.

Figures, though. The greedy, little bastard still swallowed down my bait...

His eyes rolled, but from the overflowing backpack nearby, he produced another impostor-shaped lure, this time resembling the fry of a rainbow trout. With his head remaining low, he methodically worked to restore his rig.

But, I suppose we are just the same out here, aren't we?
Always taking, taking, taking...

After tightening the necessary knots, he once more stood to take his place at the railing.

Well... at the end of the day, isn't it just in our nature?
To take so that we can live?

He sucked his teeth.

She did always say that I'm just like my father...

With the line still readied in his hand, he cast a double take at the other pole since assigned to the descender. Finding the line slack and crimped, he squinted in confusion, before turning his head to take in the familiar presence now bobbing upon the surface of the water just ahead.

... What the hell? ...

Drifting slowly and helplessly toward the horizon, the rockfish, still stunned and rigid in this state, drew from Glenn a deepening frown. Setting down the fishing pole against the rail, he grabbed the other and started reeling back in the descender.

It must have slipped free from the clamp, I guess?
Well... I can't say I didn't try...
For once...

The light departed from his eyes as they turned down once more onto the sea. Eventually, the tool emerged but when it arrived in his palm, all he could do was hold it for a moment. After snapping out of his trance, he tested the tension between the clamps with his thumb, only to find that they were eager to adhere to the shape of his knuckle. Confused, his face warped, and reluctantly he returned it to the spacious confines of his waterproof jacket.

Whatever. Just an offering for seagulls now...
...

The rockfish continued to shrink with distance.

I'm...
I'm sorry...

His thoughts were interrupted by the violent shudder coaxed out of him from the curl of a whistling, wet wind.

Good grief...

He folded his arms tight.

It's always so cold out here...

The spittle of the ocean's breath clung to his face, thickening over his worn features like a mask.

Almost feels like it gets colder every time, too...

Once more, he turned his attention back toward the fish, though his brow creased upon finding that it had somehow completely vanished from his view. His head swiveled in every direction, expecting that maybe the current had changed, or that an animal would surface nearby but the sea remained quiet and vacant.

Odd... I hadn't heard a thing...
...
If something had snatched it... or if it had finally stirred, I...
I think I would have heard the splash...

His eyes widened briefly and he wagged his head as though to physically reject this conundrum.

Whatever, I guess...
Probably went off to fish heaven then...

Snorting, he dropped the line back into the sea, but with confusion still lingering, his finger tapped restlessly against the rolling spool. The line unraveled quickly again as the weight carried his hook back down toward the secretive sea floor. His chin dipped and his eyes grew narrow as he failed at first to stop obsessing over this stupid question. Eventually, he felt as though he was finally ready to dismiss it, but these thoughts were then taken from him, suddenly and by force, as something strong yanked violently against the line.

"Whoa! What the hell?"

Taken off guard, he nearly toppled over the rail, but as he regained himself enough to start reeling, he found that this tug did not quite match the familiar feeling of any mouth or tail he had ever snagged against the hook. Rather, it reminded him of hands, pulling with the sorts of patterns and strength that his mind was taken back to days past, to the hard-fought games of tug-o-war he had played on the old, cracking schoolyard.

The pole curled forward. He twisted mightily against the stiff handle, now digging its way into his palm, but abruptly the spool froze and the line snapped taut with tension. Rearing back, he pulled hard until the rod simply snapped apart. With dull pain coursing up the length of his back, he came to just to find himself seated on the soaked floor of the steeply tilting deck. There, moisture from the puddle surrounding him seeped in through his clothing to cling onto his bruising skin.

Letting go of the splintered pole, he scrambled forward with haste, but with another tip of the deck, he quickly lost his grip. Fumbling against the momentum and along the slick wood, he slid hard into the rails. Wrapping his arms around their posts, he managed to steady himself, and when he summoned the courage to look below, all he found were the usual ballrooms of tiny, dancing jellyfish twisting in their playful circles. Calmly, they pocked the ocean's surface before being sucked beneath the hull of the aimlessly meandering boat.

With disbelief, his head turned to take in what had become of his once sturdy and flexible pole. Multiple scenarios of varying feasibility presented theories for his consideration, but then, and with a sharp hiss, the unmistakable expulsion of a whale's spout snatched his attention back onto the sea. Water, briny and viscous this time, spattered across his face and dripped from his chin, but to his ongoing perplexity, the huge meniscus of the water did not stir with any evidence of life. Rather its rhythmic waves persisted without sound, shadow, or ripples.

All the while still scouring the surface for answers, he stumbled back onto his feet again. Despite the lack of what should have been a magnificent presence and settling on the seemingly obvious conclusion, he couldn't restrain a short and stupid chuckle.

"Well…" He shrugged loosely. "I suppose that might be the biggest thing I've ever set a hook on." Glenn mumbled, to no one in particular. "--shame I couldn't quite land it... Now that would be quite the tale, wouldn't it? ..."

Something heavy landed with a thump on the deck behind him, and he flinched. Attention instantly switching toward the noise, he squinted, only to find that nothing was there.

91

"..."

He stared at this space for a while but eventually managed to convince himself that he remained alone. Brow lifting, he shook his head and resumed searching the water for any sign of this supposed whale. However, his eyes darted aimlessly with distraction.

And to think... people pay such big money for a chance to catch a glimpse of these stupid sea cows...

"Hmph." He tried hard to take his mind elsewhere.

I wonder if I could start a business...

He froze, recognizing the beat of heavy footsteps suddenly materializing along the deck behind him. The muscles of his face slackened with suspense, and though it frightened him on an instinctual level, his head began to turn around on its own reluctant accord. At first, empty space greeted the corner of his eye again, but upon turning further to take in the full length of the deck, the sight he soon beheld forced him to wear his budding confusion on his face.

Standing in the midst of a shallow, but newly formed puddle, a single, mottled seagull vacantly returned his stare. Yet, something about its stance felt unusually still and focused, as though it were somehow reading the wavelengths of his conflicting, befuddled thoughts. For what felt like a long time, he peered back into the black pinpoints of its eyes, until they shrunk, and rolled somewhere behind the clear membrane of its sliding eyelids.

All at once, its head curled backward, and he flinched upon it aggressively shambling forward in his direction. Startled by its unnatural posture, his mouth cracked into the suggestion of amusement or incredulity, he couldn't quite choose, but before his lips could even form the shape of a word, the bird's gullet inflated and exploded into a loud, and syncopated bellow.

Hwaaa! Ha ha ha ha--!

It was a sound he had heard many, many times, no matter where he would travel along these rocky coastlines. It could have been the pungent streets of the bay front, or from the pinnacle of his neighbors' gables, he knew this call intimately. Yet something about it this time still met his ear in an unsettling way. It cloyed deep, and at this moment, he couldn't help but feel as though it were belting out some sort of specific message. An angry holler, a cruel mockery, or even an ominous warning, he couldn't quite decipher it. Upon winding to the end of its breath, the bird inhaled again, and more forcefully flung forth its voice.

Hwaaaaaaaaa!

His eyes shifted and snapped across the sky as he came to a realization.

Just the one?
Strange...

...
I mean... Don't they... normally hang out in flocks?

His gaze swiveled across various points of the empty fog surrounding him, but ever perpetual was the silver sea churning and swirling like muddied paint, forever over-mixing into an expanse of shadows and reflections he couldn't quite tease apart. Through the thickening inversion, he could no longer sense the horizon, never mind the lights of any distance ships; all he beheld were the twisting, sticky mists. Frowning, he began to realize that he had arrived at the very mouth of that void he had so foolishly taunted across the hours, but bringing him back to the present, footfall drummed against his ear once again.

The sound, unusually weighted for just a bird, was quick this time. It was as though their possessor were accelerating to charge. He spun around, expecting to find the creature snapping at his toes, but he did not. Rather, it wasn't until he took in the vacant deck that he realized that silence had since eerily blanketed his environment and abruptly neutralized the bird's obnoxious laughter.

It was just as he was starting to process this change that a persistent tapping began to reflect off the bow of the boat. Through the boards, this sensation reverberated up into his feet where it evolved into a maddening noise, constantly repeating itself and boring its way back into his head. The boat lurched rigidly, forcing him to realize that something strong had just pushed it off its path. He hesitated to turn, but when he peered over the railing, the sight of a small, strange dingy prompted the blood to turn still within his veins.

Barnacles crusted its splintered, warped wood, and despite the wake unfurling from the walls of his vehicle, the strange dinghy seemed to teeter calmly, almost playfully, as though possessing some sort of eager curiosity to tag along for whatever journey.

"Hmph." Regaining composure, he snickered and anchored his hands onto his waist. "Well, how about that?"

Lucky me, I guess... Free boat...

From where the crab pot used to reside, he reached for the multicolored pile of beaten, tangled ropes. The first one that he tugged upon came free with suspicious ease, and as he brought it to his eye, he found it to be impractically short and roughly frayed at either end.

Weird... His eyes narrowed, and with a limp toss, he simply cast it overboard. Watching it sink, he mulled, *Well, I don't remember that one tearing... but... Okay... Just trash then...*

With some effort and puzzle-solving, he separated another rope from the pile. After another brief visual inspection, he could identify it was also a bit worse for wear, but following a few forceful tugs between his hands, he still determined that it would be suitable enough for the task at hand.

Unconsciously biting his tongue, he aimed first and then tossed the end of the rope toward the center of the dinghy. Landing softly, it coiled into a loose pile, and with the help of an old gaff once propped along the rod rack nearby, he clumsily finagled the tether around the molded board of the stool. He knelt again, reaching long between the railings to grip the other end of the rope as he maneuvered it back into his awaiting hand.

I don't know why, but... it almost feels like I was meant to find this...
Like this is some encounter, driven by fate.

He smirked against a silly thought.

What if I got in?

As tight as he could manage, he fastened both ends into a knot around the aluminum banister of his boat's railing. Taking in the dinghy for another time, it didn't seem to be particularly special or even in good shape; nothing to justify this weird feeling of attachment, though he continued to proudly admire the rare find anyway.

Poor little thing looks so old... like it's been out here for years and years...
Could be even an antique...

More unscrupulously, he pondered, *Hell... maybe it's worth a pretty penny...*

After all... He began to wring his hands. *–there's always some idiot who'll drop even stupider cash on anything with an interesting story...*

Then again...

His head began to slowly tilt.

I can't help but feel as though it's somehow kind of... familiar...

Intrustrive was the hazy memory of fishing with his father in the murky channels of the Big Creek Reservoir. It was just as he was beginning to piece together the make of that old, little boat that the clear sound of a human voice yanked him back into reality.

"Hey."

Straightening instantly, he peeked across his shoulder, only to find that the seagull had returned. Motionlessly it was perched upon the corner of the stern and once more, it vacuously stared back at him. Its attention even persisted in his peripheral as he slowly lowered his head to process what had just occurred.

Eyes fluttering, he laughed and shook his head. "Oh wow... Am I hearing things..." Joking, he peered back at the bird and boldly asked, "That wasn't you now, was it?"

The seagull released a low, long grumble, as though it were trying to offer some kind of response to his jest. Smile fading, they once more engaged in another staring contest, for what felt like an awkwardly long time. Becoming irritated, Glenn hopped to his feet all at once and bellowed, "Alright! I've had enough of you! Go on! Get out of here! G'it!"

Baffled, his wide posture deteriorated when the bird did not even budge. Rather, it merely cocked its head, briefly tracking another dramatic swing of Glenn's arm before latching to his gaze again with a single, asynchronous blink. Further strange was the way that the rolling of the waves seemed to recede into nothing all at once.

"Glenn."

This time, he recognized the impossibly masculine voice materializing right behind him, but with his terrified gaze still locked onto that of the seagull, he couldn't bring himself to turn and look.

I'm... I'm just imagining things...

96

His breath rattled uncomfortably between his teeth.

I've been out here thinking so much... that I'm... I'm starting to imagine things...

He laughed nervously and placed his palm on his forehead, only to find that it was clammy and cold.

I feel fine at least...

Patiently, the seagull observed him but Glenn snarled and ducked his way back into the cabin for privacy. Through the back window, he watched the seagull diligently track him with slow, deliberate swivels of its head. Unsettled, the hair on the back of Glenn's neck began to rise and he took a cautious seat behind the wheel.

What the fuck does this stupid thing want? Huh?

His head turned the other way. Through the other window, he could see his bait, completely exposed within the opening of the backpack.

Maybe that's it?
Maybe it's just waiting until I'm not looking?
They are crafty like that... So, that has to be it...

He looked back, expecting that the bird would start to waddle its way over to this tempting haul, but to his surprise, it had since vanished for another time.

"..."

He sat there, staring at where it had been for a while. Reluctantly, he figured, *Okay... So, it must have just flown off then... That shouldn't be surprising, that's what they do...*

He turned forward in the seat again. Stiffened by the cold, he feverishly rubbed his aching hands together, but when the friction failed to spark warmth, he cupped them to his face and instead tried to bathe his palms with the weak, humid heat of several deep breaths. As he did this, he stared into the thin air, unable to shake the image of the seagull's expectant wide stare.

You know what?
Let's just go... somewhere else...

He laughed with embarrassment.

A bird, of all things...

After flexing his fingers for another time, he sniffled back his running snot and fumbled across the top of the console for the small, silver key. Pushed clumsily by his numb extremities, it nearly slipped onto the ground, but having caught it by its buoyant fob, he bettered his grip and jammed it into the ignition.

Hang on... What's all this?

He paused, noticing strange scratches in the aluminum surrounding key hole. With his thumb, he began to scratch at these abrasions, before escaping his distraction and giving the key a hurried twist.
The engine clicked uselessly.
Perplexed, he tried again, but with every attempt, he was greeted by harrowing silence. His eyes snapped onto the gauge, where to his ongoing confusion, the dial leaned in stasis just over the half-fill mark.

Should it be doing that when it's off...?
I mean... either way, I know for a fact that I'm good on gas...

Next, he looked to the throttle, only to find it in the neutral position where it belonged.

"What the hell.."

Again, he tried at the key, becoming more frustrated and forceful with every additional twist.

"Why?" He grimaced. "Why are you doing this? … You useless thing…"

With a defeated huff, he slouched back against the seat and helplessly scoured the instruments of the console. Then, with a shake of his head, he sat up again and yanked the nearby radio from its hook. He mashed on the button meant to bring it to a channel, and though he expected to be greeted by static and the typically banal conversations from nearby ships, the speaker merely popped once, loudly, before delivering ear-ringing silence.

Desperately, he held down the push-to-talk button and tried to speak into the device anyway.

"Hello? Hello? Can anyone hear me?"

He could tell by the flatness of his voice that it merely deflected off the speaker, unable to be absorbed and transmitted. Wide-eyed, all he could do now was stare at the microphone, all the while grappling with the reality of his situation and the frightening implications that came with it.

Whatever…

Tapping his fingers against the device, he tried to reason with himself.

She's an old gal after all…
I'm sure after a little bit, I can try again and surely, the engine will–

Something rapped loud against the window, with enough force that he could see the glass rattle in his peripheral. Startled, he hunched. Slowly surfacing in the corner of his eye, there arrived the suggestion of a humanoid figure, standing where the dinghy should have been and waving excitedly for his attention. Its shape and movements were stark and undeniable. Visibly trembling now, his knuckles paled as they tightened around the unresponsive microphone.

No...
This isn't... right...
...
This isn't real...

His chin began to turn toward the figure, but stopping himself, he determined,

No...
Don't look at it...

"Glenn."

Instead, he dared to turn his head in the opposite direction. Though the vacancy of these windows, full of empty gray on this side, brought him some relief, he couldn't quite shake the presence still lingering outside at his back. A cold draft from somewhere unknown licked a humid path up the slope of his neck and crested over the top of his head. Though it felt petulant and pathetic after all of his previous tantrums, he determined,

Home...
I have to get home...

The dinghy continued to tap softly at the bow of the ship, as though to insist that it was still there and waiting for him. With such a pattern, he determined that there was no way anyone could be standing upright in the vessel without losing their balance, nor should they have even been tall enough to peer over the edge of the ship in that way. Emboldened by logic, he finally twisted his head around to look, but there, he couldn't tell if the unoccupied space was relieving or further, deeply disquieting.

... It's empty...
It has to be... I saw it...
How could there be anyone there...?
Right?
I... I'm imagining things. Hearing things...

Reluctantly emerging from the cramped shelter of the cabin, his foot overlapped with something gooey, and he slipped. He managed to catch himself on the surrounding frame, but he instantly froze upon taking in the new condition of the deck. Like raindrops, spherical, gelatinous little bodies of moon jellies freckled the boards in a winding path, all the way down to the very tips of his worn-down boots. This time, he could not stop his inquiring gaze from following them back to their source.

There, on the lip of the gunwale, he observed a seagull, hunched and fixated on something down below. After a moment that seemed to emulate thought, it expanded its wings, and hopped silently over the edge, toward the surface of the water. Glenn gawked at the vacated railing, expecting to hear a splash, but he did not. Out of morbid curiosity or foolishness, he couldn't quite tell, he was compelled to step forth to find out where it could have possibly gone.

Holding his breath, he was slow to peer over the railing, but the sickening smell met his nostrils first.

To his horror, the tiny dinghy was overflowing with the rigid bodies of lifeless seagulls, contorted, often without feathers, and skeletal with varying states of decay. Flies circled the heap, buzzing loudly now, and as the bones began to squirm, the more precariously piled seagulls toppled over and rolled into the water with soft, but jarring, repeated splashes. His heart stopped hard in his chest and though he felt the need to scream, the air within him stayed trapped inside a lump in the middle of his throat. His thoughts flurried with almost painful pangs of horror and confusion, but his mouth could only gape and quiver with small, stifled huffs of incoherence.

With sudden motion signaling his attention, his eyes switched up in time just to connect with the unblinking, black stare of a seal, its head just barely rising above the water's solid surface. Gaze never wavering, it began to sink slowly, straight down into the depths again, but it moved so unnaturally that it was as though something bigger was gently pulling it downward by its tail.

Falling onto his knees, he began to grapple clumsily at the knot of the rope. As the dinghy, heavy now, tried to pull his groaning boat toward an unknown direction, the tether began to tighten around the railing like a fist determined to hang on. Flies began to tickle and nibble at his face, and as he struggled, he refused to look directly at the dinghy.

Fingers shaking, he clawed and dug into the tightly bound knurls, with such desperation that his nail beds began to crack, break, and slowly bleed in thin rivers down his knuckles. Finally regaining sense, he reared back and fumbled through his pockets for a small knife. Water droplets leaped from its edge as he flicked it open, but quick was the thin blade to dull as he sawed frantically through the braided twine. When the tool could no longer cut, he flung it onto the deck, where it bounced, slid, and rolled down toward the stern. Against the intense lifting of an angry wave, water exploded against the boat's nose, and the knife was hurled into the sea.

With his hands again, he grabbed the rope and pulled hard against the fray. For a moment, he even considered using his teeth though he knew couldn't bear to taste whatever rotten brine it had surely absorbed. He audibly grimaced against the straining of his arms, his voice breaking all the while with terror and exhaustion. The threads tore apart one by one, eventually winding down to the very last connective cord. Upon finally separating, the rope burned hot across the surface of his palm as it whipped violently back between the rails. Perhaps not registering this fresh pain amid his adrenaline, he scrambled forth just in time to watch the tattered end of the rope disappear into the black, breaking shadows of the water.

Calmly, the dinghy rotated and started to drift away. Struggling for breath, he diligently watched on to ensure that it would truly sink back into the incoming fog to hopefully return to whatever Hell from which it spawned. Through the waves, it traveled unnaturally; straight, fast, and steady as though propelled by an invisible motor, or even worse, some kind of sentient intention. It was just as he was beginning to consider the possibility that it was acting with purpose that a colossal outline took shape behind the walls of mist and cast over him an engulfing shadow.

Hwaaaaaa! Hwaaa hwaaa! Ha ha ha ha ha!

Gigantic, pale sails rose tall above the fog, and they floated forward so smoothly it was as though this great ship was simply cutting its path through the skies. While its mighty, ornately carved hull materialized with such commanding stature, its movements did not cast a wake. It moved silently somehow, as though existing on a plane entirely separate from this reality.

From its towering masts to its web-like shrouds, and all along the length of its long, pointed bowsprit, it teemed with the clamor of swarming birds. The wind blew hard, carrying toward him the stink of stagnant waters, musty dander, and the festering, stale impressions of avian excrement.

Stunned, all he could do was kneel there as it revealed itself segment by mighty segment. From its many gunports, where the barrels of cannons should have peeked, it instead spewed green, winding, and glowing mists, with these patterns occasionally disrupted by the passage of infinite seagulls. Restlessly, the birds constantly traded spots between the sloop's many perches, and swaying soundlessly, a huge, broken chain dangled limply from its hip where its anchor should have been. Stuffed within the huge eye of every link, crowds of birds stared back at Glenn, filling every new second with their raucous chuckling.

As the dusty wings of a seagull grazed the back of his head with its passage, he flinched and cowered. Yet, as he tracked its trajectory from beneath the shelter of his arms, it led his eye onto the conspicuous object balancing precariously at the end of a thin, protruding plank.

Wait a second...

He zeroed in on this single humanoid shape. It walked backward onto the deck, before appearing to lean over the edge of the thick, ornate oaken gunwale. There, the figure began waving both arms in a repetitive, insistent, and beckoning sort of motion. More troubling, and despite the distortions of distance, he found that it possessed a certain shape of familiarity. Frantically he scoured the archives of his memory until, like rubble, the realization crashed down upon all of his senses at once.

That...
That looks like my father...

The once discordant screams of the seagulls joined together in a violent chorus. Like thunder, the sound quailed above the clouds, shaking the very ocean and rattling the boards beneath his knees.

But that can't be...
He's dead...

As though privy to these thoughts, the figure suddenly stopped and assumed a more rigid stance. There, and without face, it merely returned Glenn's stare through the curling inversions, as though waiting for him to produce another thought.

He's been dead...

Unbeknownst to him was his breath now departing his nostrils in cold fogs. Above his head, another seagull glided gracefully in a wide, silent circle before taking its perch on the railing of his boat's increasingly crowded stern.

No...

He remained oblivious to their staring.

I have to get out of here...

Finally managing to break free from his trance enough to rise, he began to back away until his shoulders collided with the windows of the cabin behind him. Against the ongoing hollering of roaring birds, their glass shook and cracked along their seals.

But the boat...

His expression warped with terror as he ducked under the doorway and dove into the seat behind the wheel. Through the roof, and like a torrent of rain, he was surrounded by the soft pattering of webbed feet landing in random spots upon the metal.

It...
What if it won't start again...?

He didn't even dare look up as he fumbled the key from his pocket. In his peripheral, he could see bird after bird descending and landing in orderly lines along the ship's railings. But unlike those on the massive ship ahead, they stayed silent and closely observant of his actions. Within his shaking hand, the teeth of the key danced around the ignition in circles, scratching grooves into the metal with every failed attempt at insertion.

But, I have to try...

His fingers crumpled painfully against the lacquered surface of the dash as the key finally slotted into place. As he twisted it forward, he could barely believe his ears when the engine roared with the presence of life. Exhaling, his mouth cracked open into a brief, faltering grin, and wasting no more time, he clutched the throttle and jerked it forward as far as it would allow. The boat sputtered and choked, before launching forward into a wild charge. With a twist of the wheel, it spun sharply, scooping up water with the intensity of its tilt. Flung from their perches, the seagulls lifted in synchronized formations and glided backward, into the sky, where they were further lifted by the swelling winds. Even from where they floated, they continued to observe the fleeing vessel, but eventually, and one by one, they returned to the phantom ship now submerging itself back into mists.

The hollering of the birds began to gradually dissipate beneath the roar of the straining engine. He looked backward, over his shoulder, and felt some comfort to find that the giant ghost ship made no apparent movement to suggest it would pursue him. Rather, it continued idly upon its original trajectory, with its loyal thralls, now tiny with distance and dancing around its fading silhouette like an infestation of bouncing fleas. Still, he couldn't quite shake the lingering feeling that it had been seeking him in particular, that it wanted something from him. Thinking back on the dinghy, and how it so quickly scrambled back to the protection of the ship's mighty hull, he felt nauseous upon wondering what may have happened if he had ever humored the idea of boarding it.

He pushed harder against the throttle, but it could not lean any further. Even so, his hand remained glued there, trembling and pallid with residual fear.

What...
What did I just witness?

He couldn't tell if it was humidity or sweat forming beads along his forehead.

Seriously...
What in the hell was that?

Though his eyes snapped restlessly with thought, they couldn't seem to attach to anything in particular.

.... And what did it want?

He stared anxiously into the fog, hoping to see it break away into the harbor. Obsessively he recounted the trip and all of its surreal moments, but he failed to make sense of them, however fresh.

Just a dream...
It has to be...
This is... all just a bad dream...

I'll wake up…
With the fishing pole shaking between my hands…

He looked down at his fingernails, now bruising purple from his struggle with the rope. Once more registering their state, they began to tangibly sting, with a warm pain throbbing to the rhythm of his panicked pulse.

But… why?

His eyes narrowed and shifted restlessly against this question. Like delicate steam gently lifting from a hot spring, thin plumes of fog washed past the boat as it carved a furious trail back toward the bay.

What did they want?

The wild choir of the ghost ship's wailing weaved stubbornly between his thoughts, not unlike a terrible song now stuck forever in his head.

They seemed angry… angry at me…
But what have I done?
What did I do to… deserve any of that?
Am I really that… bad of a person?

The colossal arch of the bridge emerged suddenly but gloriously from the dense inversions belching from the mouth of the bay.

"Finally…" His voice quaked upon escaping him.

With the promise of safety, he cut the engine for the sole purpose of simply catching his breath. Frenzied, his heart raced. It was as though he had become an extremity of the boat on their desperate race to come back home.

… Thank God…

His eyes swelled wide with disbelief.

I made it…

He pawed at his legs and pockets, before clumsily producing his cell phone from the zippered pocket on his breast. Covetously now, he clutched the device between both of his pruned hands, but as he mentally sifted through the faces of family and friends, he scoffed incredulously, and realized,

But… who…
Who would even believe me?

Relieved but also surprised to see that the phone still possessed a charge, he switched it on, and eagerly this time, scoured the entirety of the unread message.

When are you going to come home, Glenn? We're getting worried…

His eyes fluttered. At first, he began to smile with relief, familiarity, and amusement, up until he realized that the time stamp of the message suggested it had originated several years in the past.

"What the…"

Like a cascade, texts from various numbers began to flood the tiny screen, often overlapping one another with the rapidity in which they appeared.

Glenn?? We miss you… please call. We're

Where are you? Are you okay? I

Hey so… Daisy said you left? Why didn't y

Dad, what the hell

Please answer… we've contacted the police…

So, I came to your funeral and…

Mutating with horror, his eyes switched upward through the windshield. There, perched patiently on the familiar, old crab trap tucked snug in the corner of the deck, waited a mottled seagull. When their gazes locked, its gullet became swollen, and though it parted its beak to call out, all that met Glenn's ear was the cruel ringing of resonating silence.

Again, the phone vibrated in his palm with another incoming message, but this time, he couldn't bring himself to look.

... No...

The device slipped through his fingers and broke apart on the deck where its fragments began to disappear.

Please...

He began to weep.

I just want to see my family again...
I take it all back...

Like a vignette sadistically swallowing his last window into the reality he had left behind, nightfall rapidly began to close around his view of the bay. The last light of what he thought to be the harbor instantly blinked out of existence. He looked up, expecting that the evening stars would take their place, but they did not. Rather, the spreading, dark clouds bled seamlessly into the fog, seemingly eager to inhale him backward in time once again. Panicked, he thought to reach out to these impressions of the shore, but he could not. Instead, the once recognizable shape of his hand burst into feathers that curled with a flurry into the enveloping darkness all around him.

Please... Whatever you are...

Vision blurring, he could see the suggestion of the seagull pacing slowly in his direction.

Just give me another chance...

Secrets of Those Lost to the Sea

By Maizey Gardiner

Pop-pop always warned me never to explore when the tide was coming in. I guess this is why.

My family was taking too long, so I just wandered off. it was only for a minute. When I turned around, they were gone, almost as if I had been there alone for hours.

I found a cave. I wasn't sure what was in it. I thought maybe my family went in. I just looked around quickly, but even then, the tide came in too fast for me to escape. I wasn't thinking.

The water is already covering my ankles. It's freezing as I splash, running around to every edge looking for a way out.

The water Is blocking all exits. I'm scared. I look everywhere— nothing. But when I look up I see a cave! it is almost impossible to get to. It's at least fifteen feet off the ground In the wall. There is a wall of rocks that I can try to climb up to the cave. It's either that or drowning because the water is up to my knees now.

I reach with my left, then my right hand finding sharp rocks to hold onto, jumping. I push both feet onto the wall and begin the climb. I can feel the skin peeling off both of my hands, my fingertips are tingling with the blood swelling. I have to be very careful. One wrong move and I can be done. Never seen again. Fish food.

I pull myself up over the ledge. The cave isn't as big as I thought. It's just barely taller than me and not much bigger than my parent's bathroom. The battery on my dad's old iPhone is at 8%, that's enough to use the flashlight, but not for long and I don't know how long until the tide goes back out. I could be here for a week or maybe even a year. Maybe the tide will NEVER go back out. Maybe this is where I die.

Scanning the cave with the flashlight I can see that this isn't a natural cave. It was carved out, man-made for sure. All the walls are smooth except for a couple of carvings of stick-figure girls, rather than the regular triangle dresses it almost looks like a fishtail instead of legs. I don't know if climbing up to this cave was a good idea, but it was my only chance of not dying. And now the water is only inches away from the ledge I'm standing on. It reminds me of the poem where the boy is being eaten by a boa constrictor. In a minute I'll be saying "Oh fiddle oh fiddle, it's up to my middle."

The water won't stop rising and there is nowhere for me to go. This is it. The end of Emily. I should have at least told Jeremy where Mom keeps her secret snack stash. That would have been a good big sister move. Hopefully, he figures it out, because with the water licking my chin, I won't be going home.

I close my eyes accepting my fate. Something cold yet soft presses up against my nose. My eyes shoot open and I'm met with a face. A young face, maybe 4 or 5 years old. I didn't see anyone else in the cave, who else was stupid enough to get caught in the rising tide? Her neck is lined with slices, except they're not slices, they're gills. It's like something out of a mermaid movie.

The little girl swims up to the walls with the carvings and presses a carving into the wall. It surprises me, but maybe it's a way out. I rush to the wall just as it opens.

There are at least twenty Mermaids in the water.

The other Mermaids stare at me. I am usually very shy but it feels right to be here. Like I belong.

The little Mermaid swims up to me and grabs my hand pulling me into the deep water, my feet can't find the bottom, but I don't feel panicked. My feet no longer need land.

"I am Lela," She says.
"I'm Emily," I answer.

Swimming, she pulls us to a woman in a crown.

"Meet my new friend, Emily," she says.

The woman is tall and looks like a grown-up, but a young one. The way she smiles at me makes my whole insides feel happy and at peace.

"Hello, Emily. You're one of us now." The kind woman says. "Umm Okay?" I say.

I look around and see something that looks like a little island and it has girl clothes that look like they are my size like they knew I was coming. I lock up. It's flight, fight, or freeze and I am frozen.

"What is going on?" I shout, not scared, just confused. "We were once you. Those who get lost at sea become one of us for all eternity."

Looking around I see that many of the faces are familiar. I've seen news stories about them. All thought to be dead, yet here they are, saved. Living new lives, together.

I don't feel scared or worried any longer. I feel at peace, like this is where I'm meant to be.

Truth

By Leah Shrifter

A couple of years before the Covid pandemic, I joined the gathering at Newport City Hall for the Women's March. I had not made or brought my own sign to carry, and I noticed there were many copies for the taking and displaying of a heartfelt sign. Each of the identical signs was painted in bright contrasting colors and clearly lettered in three languages: Spanish, English, and what I presumed was Arabic judging from the script. The signs professed welcome and caring for all persons, regardless of race, language, country of origin, and also, as implied by the Arabic writing, religion.

All peoples and their cultures welcomed, respected, cared for. That is what I want to stand for, too. I came here to participate in the March to say that and more.

Yet, I did not pick up a sign. I wished, instead of Arabic writing, Islamic religious symbols had been pictured and a woman in a burka, since this was a Women's March. When I saw the Arabic writing, I remembered my girlhood when my grandparents, my beloved "Bubbie and Zadie," and other relatives lived in Israel in the years during and around the 1967 Six Day Arab-Israeli War. It was one of the short-term wars when the Arab nations that surrounded coastal Israel vowed to drive all the Jews into the Mediterranean Sea. No one went into the sea. In six days the Israelis soundly defeated their attackers in battle.

As a Jewish child, I learned from my venerated elders, in the black-and-white way that a child learns, that every Arab hated us and wished us dead. As an adult, I have spent many years unlearning my blanket fears, and I am still working on it. I remind myself that not all Muslims are Arabs, and not all Arabs are Muslims. Doubtless, there are exceptions, but I do not expect someone of Muslim faith to hate me, nor do I fear a Muslim as I would a contemporary Nazi, if I were to meet up with him.

Still, there was an undercurrent of fear or distrust that ran through me when I saw the Arabic writing on the colorful signs painted for the Women's March. My elders, the family I loved who loved me, could not help but share their fears with me. So I told myself I have a responsibility to keep my feelings in perspective and remember they are old fears and probably unnecessary in Newport, Oregon.

I do the best I can with my ambivalence, but that day I did not carry the sign in the Women's March. I confess it in writing.

A Mere Slip of a Girl

By L.W. Smolen

For some strange reason, even though it has been three years since she was taken by the consumption, I can see my older sister Gladdie's beautiful face plainly through our ceiling. The pall of longing ever in her lonely eyes, Gladdie rivaled no Yaquina girl, for I knew she had buried her heart at her young man's grave in Philomath where we lived during 1872.

They found a body on the beach today. My Father heard it while he was south at Seal Rocks because Bennie Collins's boat was in danger. They think I'm asleep with the consumption, but I can hear them in the kitchen. They said the dead man was quite tall. The men said it was nothing but an Indian that cut his own throat, but they flushed the turkey vultures and dragged it out of the driftwood, and buried it right there. They said burying an Indian was government work and being as there was plenty of room on the new combined Reservation and "no Indian should oughtta been on the beach near town without a pass from the Superintendent anyhow," they just dug shallow. The men being burdened taxpayers besides, they said shallow was good enough, as turkey vultures don't dig.

Most folks in Newport think it was maybe a renegade some people call Charlie Taylor, but I know it wasn't. Charlie Taylor's hiding up at his sister's right now.

I'm the only girl left in our family. My Mother says "No, dear", but I know it's my time to die – just like my three sisters, all wasted by the consumption, my brothers spared. I can feel myself coming out of my skin - drifting away - just going and starting to fly free on the summer Trades. My chest isn't hurting right now so I've got nothing to do but lay here thinking about a dead Indian. They lived all over here before us, but you pretty much just can't know it by looking around.

It must already be afternoon. I can hear the wind – the Northwest Trades rumbling in our stone chimney.

That day, I folded my dress. I never told anyone that he saw me. I never told.

Our house is so quiet! The rumble of the Trades is a voice. I know what it is telling me today.

Public School here is just during the Summer. Instead, in private, during winter, my Mother used to school me and at least a dozen other children – charged their parents a "plenty high" two-bits tuition per week – taught us eight months straight. That year, we got done early. Only I could easily read and understand even the books the schooners brought us out of California where new books came up around The Horn from Europe. Mother said she couldn't give me a public award because she was the Teacher and so people would talk. She told me I'm not a student, but a "true scholar" and so instead of an award with my name on it, she made me a new flannel dress. She didn't have buttons, so she designed it as a wrap-around with a sewn-on belt that went through a slit at the waist and tied in front. The collar flared and stood up with real style. Down my left leg were three small ties that kept the bottom of my dress from blowing open. Some Newport girls told me I "flaunt" in it. They spoke true.

Why my Mother and Father have loved me as they do, I don't know. I am prideful and disobedient. From an early age, I would roam for many hours and return home to find my Mother, her fears driving her to tears. On one of my selfish junkets, I learned that every Spring, there's a little cliff flower with a yellow button center and lime-colored lettuce leaves that hug the ground. If you're daring, you can pick them free, way out on Yaquina Head up high above where the sea birds all nest. My sisters – Gladdie, Loie, and Iris - are all buried in a row up on Palatine Hill above Yaquina Head overlooking the vast Pacific. I used to risk picking the little cliff flowers for their graves.

I guess I did fall asleep a while ago. It's dark out now. I'm all damp and chilling from the night sweats. My Mother is here beside my bed. She looks very serious and teary all at the same time. I wish I could make her feel better.

I think I was just now dreaming. I saw him again. Even though I know now he's dead, this time he didn't look ugly and fierce like before. Folks say some Indians have white souls inside their dark skins. I don't think so. White isn't the right color. White's too homely.

Yaquina Head is all solid rock. It sticks at least a mile into the ocean and they put a lighthouse out on the end. All along the Head, high cliffs drop to the foaming ocean far below where groups of rocks are scattered so no boat can come in safely closer than most of a mile. It is a desolate, forlorn place. The ghosts of lost fishermen and ship-wrecked sailors wander those rocks where they were drowned. Missing miserably my dead sisters, that is the very reason I walked out there quite alone the first time. That's when, in our simple life in Newport, I first saw the little button-centered flowers and I finally had something to give my sisters. That's when lonely Yaquina Head first became my own place.

Will Keady is here again to visit me. He smells so fresh and alive like the salt air off the bay. I'm quite embarrassed at my pale, sickly appearance. The new girl, Ladd Shaw, had marked him for her own. She is older and has quite a flamboyant fetch and sings the old songs like "Gypsy's Warning" beautifully, but Will would be mine forever, doubtless, if I were to live. Now, he daren't even touch my feverish hand, but I can see it in his eyes.

Everyone has gone out, to the lee side of the house, in the sun. Our house is again so still. Today, in our chimney, the Trades are a full gale. It screams a cold, summer melody.

But Will Keady has been killed! My Mother just told me this morning. She said I have slept or been delirious for over a week. She said a strange storm forced a Danish lumber schooner, its deck load torn away, into our little bay for repairs. She said the crew was three weeks starved, hardly even water. A day or so before the tide set for the schooner's departure from our little bay, the Northwest Trades brought us some very squally weather. One afternoon, Will sailed up to Oysterville with Captain Nissen (of the schooner) in the schooner's small boat to finish some business. The Oysterville reach was a ragged chop that afternoon and the wind was crossing the riptide. The Captain's body has been found very battered, but not Will's.

117

Mother has gone back out into the kitchen and she is singing quietly. I know she doesn't want to sing, but I beg her "Sing to me!" so she does, though sadly.

My eyes are closed, but I know evening is coming on. When people's voices inside our house stop, I hear the wind hushed down now to a moan.

Just now, I felt a dark shadow pass over my bed. My eyes are closed, but I could feel him.

I know tomorrow, the Trades will take us both.

I can never, never tell. His shadow just now has made me suddenly remember details I haven't thought of for a long, long time. It was a morning to make the blood quicken in one's veins and in my new "flaunt" dress, I pilgrimaged alone to Yaquina Head. That time, I brought along a basket Old Mary, wife No. 2 to California Jack who was brought up the Coast when they condensed the Indian Agencies, had given me. In it, I carried a small lunch of bread and dried apples. I wanted to not be distracted by hunger. I wanted Gladdie, Loie, Iris, and myself to have occasion to talk while I placed my little cliff flowers on their graves, but we never did.

Out onto Yaquina Head, I walked in the lonely sunshine feeling beautiful and isolated as Estella in the story "Great Expectations." Even though great huge waves were rolling in off the deep, blue ocean far below me, the dark water rose and fell slowly over the sharp black rocks like the breast of giant, sleeping Gulliver quietly breathing. The barks of basking brown sea lions echoed up to me through the stillness of the morning.

But when I arrived at my usual flower beds, I felt a sudden, stinging pang. I discovered that I had been invaded. A stranger had picked all my flowers and so I began to think of a route around the salal walls that commanded Yaquina Head.

The wagon road to the Yaquina Head lighthouse runs to the north, protected from the fierce winter gales that sweep from the open Southern ocean.

The opposite, southern edge, where I sought my little flowers in those days is smothered by an endless thicket of wind-stunted pines and fluffy myrtle floating on a sea of dark salal that stands tall as a man, and dense as the hair on a head. But Captain Wynant, a commanding officer who runs his ship never profane, lent me his long spy-glass which extends out in three sections, your eye peering through the small end. With it, I had studied the Head from a distance of over two miles.

I had seen scattered on the salal sea along the southern cliff brink, grassy islands of safety where it appeared Spring flowers might grow.

I have coughed up quite a lot of blood today. There is more pain. Our single physician in Newport, Doctor Hoag, a pleasant man and kind, can really do nothing for me but sometimes bring my fever under control. Doctor Hoag is here now. I can hear him and my Mother murmuring somewhere distant. They can't know of the shadow which I felt pass over me just moments ago. I sense him near me. Now, I see there is no longer a scar across his throat.

I remember, though very dismayed at first on discovering my flowers all picked, I had resolved to find the islands of safety I had seen through Captain Wynant's spyglass. Salal has a beautifully smooth, red bark and it rises to the occasion exactly like myself then – skinny and spindle-legged. I remember, to save it, I took off my dress and folded it with the bodice on top so that my stylish collar could stand. In only my underthings and carrying my folded dress and basket, I stepped behind the salal curtain.

Reaching for the Sun's life, ever-dense salal formed a canopy over my head that barely parted above me as I stepped and stooped through the silent gloom. At only eleven, I was such a mere slip of a girl that I barely needed ever to push the tall stems aside. A winding dark passage yielded to me endlessly. I stopped at the white bones of a small animal that had died quite a long time ago. I crouched. I studied the skeleton intently. Since its bones were close together, I could tell it had not died a violent death – but, rather, a lonely one. When I stood back up though, thinking to check behind me, I found the salal curtain had closed back as if I had never passed there at all. I had an awful moment of confusion and panic. I had lost my way home. But then I heard my father's voice reminding me as he always used to do, "One thing at a time, Lucy."

Even though I can hear the muffled and distant mutterings of my Mother and Doctor Hoag, I am exactly alone at this my final hour. I can feel again the heat of the Sun on my Island of Safety – just as when I first burst out upon it from the salal that day – just when its warmth first touched my skin. Suddenly back in that warm sunshine, I sensed a deliciousness.

I saw far to the south, slowly crossing the bar that windless morning, the black hull of a lumber schooner entering our little bay in ballast, probably bound to lade at Puget Sound, thence San Francisco. Since Stonewall Shoal wasn't breaking, I knew the schooner was lifting on a flood tide. At the entrance to our snug harbor, up on the bluff amongst the pines, the white-painted Ocean House was plainly visible in the clear air as was below it the tip of the plank boardwalk my Father and Mr. Venables had built.

On top of my entire world, I was profoundly alone. Almost directly below me, a whale nursing its little calf drew my vision down. Just as if I were Alice, I realized I was standing at the beginning of what appeared to me as a natural stone staircase descending, and not far, before it disappeared from my sight.

I became so powerfully curious, that I felt alive beyond measure. Following the white rabbit, Alice did not hesitate. I took her example. My earlier feeling of deliciousness was replaced by a very strange sense. As I thought carefully where to place my feet and balance, I realized that long, long ago other minds had thought and chosen and stepped exactly on my same stones, descending and descending that high wall of fatal rock.

Suddenly frightened, I stood stopped, unsure of anything. I thought I should just go back. I thought helplessly of home and my Mother and how she would feel if I... but then, a cool breeze puffed up off the ocean and into my face. A wild sound rode it – the chatter of thousands of seabirds. I had never seen so many dark, diving Murres blanket the sleeping ocean.

At sea level, the rock spread and flattened nearly evenly, just as if it once were the flowing batter of fresh, morning flannel cakes poured out onto a giant griddle. For once, my poor, clumsy shoes which my Father had made me were perfect. I stood quite still again. I had been near the ocean on many occasions, but now profoundly alone in that strange, watery cathedral the salt air fairly stung my nose. I had the creepy, lonely sense that I and my dead sisters were nothing more significant than barnacles – in whose nameless faces I was stepping right then. Thinking of my lost sisters, suddenly I became so sad that I couldn't stand up. I set my folded dress and Wife No.2's spruce-root basket on a log. For a time, sitting beside them, I couldn't move at all and the warmth went out of the sun. I felt feeble and that I was in a dangerous place and that I had been a foolish, foolish child, and that my body would never ever be found.

I felt very certain that I would not die of the consumption, but of heartbreak, and that ever since Iris' death – the first of my sisters to waste and die in front of my eyes – I had been pretending. In that teeming, lonely place, nearly naked, beside what Wife No.2's dark hands had patiently made me, my mask fell away and I mourned my sisters as my childhood - that would end that very day.

Finally, through my salty veil of tears, I saw what struck me as – while I was descending earlier – a most precious gem. Very near the brink, where the flannel cake rock ended and the ocean seemed to sleep, was a deep pool somewhat larger than our small kitchen at home. The water was of the greenest emerald, its sides lined with every color of life and deep purple, spiny urchins. When I slipped my bare hand through its surface, its warmth startling me, I was suddenly flooded again by the same sense of strange deliciousness as before.

Immediately, smiling, I decided I would swim! I left my underthings and my shoes on Wife No.2's drift log and I slid and disappeared into the cool calmness of the emerald pool. I was a foolish, foolish child. One ought never to risk oneself, because others will suffer for it. Even just my bare feet in their cold - the icy Yaquina River flowing from the east into our little bay - or the ocean itself, always took my breath away. But I had never in my entire life, over my entire skin, felt such a caress as my emerald pool just then. I filled my mouth with it and rolled on my back and spouted. Above me was only the Sun and blue. A pair of seagulls chased madly across my sky. I thought stupidly of school chums Ed and Mort Abbey, who Mother scolded because they just wouldn't wash behind the ears. I felt clean and perfect. I had a very exciting thought I have never told anyone – that when my time came, I would bring my husband to that pool. I floated on my back. I closed my eyes.

But suddenly, icy cold water stopped my breath. There was a great, gushing roar. My thought was only panic. By cold ocean water, I felt myself carried up and up. I had foolishly forgotten the rogue waves that always accompany a flooding tide. My arms and legs had no force. I was lifted higher, faster. Then I dropped. I spilled. I couldn't see. The cold salt water seethed around me madly and stuffed up my nose and into my throat.

In a single moment, I saw a band of blue sky with dark, shining wet stone walls speeding right and left. Seeming to hang on wings as a hunting Eagle against the blue, the silhouette of a man with streaming long hair soared.

Then, I was lying alone beside a fire that had burnt down to embers. Its smoke filled his cave. Outside, exactly as before, the ocean seemed to sleep. Further inside, the dirt-floor cavern reached away into blackness.

Newport's native inhabitants we knew then came sixteen miles over from the Siletz Agency. They came over town for a change of scene and to sell fish to the campers from the Willamette Valley. I had seen their fishing spears with their fire-hardened points many times. Beside a bed of spruce root, some firewood, and a large, spilling pile of the black shells of the mussels that grew everywhere beside the ocean, there were only three things in his home. One was just such a fishing spear as I knew. The others were two baskets, crude compared to the fineness which Wife No.2 had given me.

When the man saw me awake, his dark face turned instantly fierce and ugly. The sight of him terrified me absolutely. I felt myself begin to shiver and shake. Vague stories of what Indians had done in olden times flooded my mind. Across his throat was a great, scarred-over gash. I saw he carried the largest knife I had ever seen. He was much taller even than Charlie Taylor and his arms and chest were bundled cords. I could see he was a hard, hard man, that he was a most dangerous, defiant renegade.

When I began to cry and wail for my mother, the anger in his face became more hideous than anyone I had ever seen. He threw up his hands just as my own Mother had done in her tears of frustration with me and my ramblings. He drew his knife and, several times with it, he made a violent slashing motion across his own throat. I was so terrified I thought, in that moment, that Gladdie, Loie, and Iris had been lucky compared to what I knew he was going to do to me.

Heavenly Father, I want to tell you now and at this, the hour of my death, that I gave not one thought to what I had done to him.

This Enchanted Place

By Brenda Buchanan Saltzer

This enchanted place where the coastal mountains greet the ocean shore was made for the young and in love...

They came upon the bramble-covered property and the rusty 'For Sale' sign on a whimsical day in March. Spring Break meant their daughters were off to visit Grandma and it was just the two of them, splurging on a spur-of-the-moment trip to the coast. The day was alive with promise.

"Come on," Claire coaxed Jack. "Let's just take a look."

He smiled at her and shook his head. "It's oceanfront property," he told her. "We can't afford it."

But he said this as he pulled the car over and began to make his way out. She always talked him into illogical things. It was what he loved most about her.

They fought their way through the overgrown thimbleberries, the salal bushes, and the dead, fallen branches of spruce and coastal pine, hearing the ocean's calming rumble before they could see the waves. And, there it was; the unimaginable, vast beauty of the Pacific coastline.

Hand in hand, they stood and took it all in—infinity and promise—the sustenance of the young and in love. The horizon stretching, the waves crashing, the gulls calling, a way down that sandy beach in front of them, non-existent today. But, they would be back. And that strip of beach would be their own. She just knew it.

So, in spite of an unpromising trip to the Newport Real Estate office, they couldn't resist making that trek through the brambles one more time before returning home. This time, she traced her finger across the 'For Sale' sign, writing the word 'SOLD' across the moss and grime on its surface.

And as she'd known would somehow happen, the little patch of oceanfront paradise-to-be became theirs. Windsong Cottage was born. It came into being with their combined labor, planning, sacrifice, and dreams. Together they built their stairway to the beach; 15 steps that opened up to them an ever-changing wonder of sand and sea. And their paradise became—not just a magical vacation getaway for them and their daughters—but a magical spot for their growing groups of friends, family, cousins, and even strangers to enjoy.

Yes, the seashore is for lovers, but it is also for families.

This enchanted place where the coastal mountains greet the ocean shore is for families…

Families love the seashore's endless possibilities and the mountain's beckoning mystery. They love campfires and colorful kites, and braving the freezing waves and building sand castles—even though they'll be washed away tomorrow. They love searching for agates, sea glass, and fossils. They love finding the sand dollars hidden in their vaults of sand. They love spotting sea lions, watching whale spouts, and seeing myriad shorebirds from seagulls to cormorants, to sandpipers. They love visiting the shell middens of the first inhabitants of the coastline. They love fishing and crabbing and digging for clams. They love surfing and kayaking in the rivers and bays. They love the hiking trails and sand dunes, the lighthouses and the aquariums, and Ripley's Believe It or Not and the Wax Works. Families love chowder, fish and chips, saltwater taffy, and shrimp cocktails, hidden cafes with menus to color, and coffee houses that serve cocoa with extra whipped cream. They love the shops with their antiques and cheap souvenirs, and browsing through dusty bookshops. They love to watch the boats in the harbor bobbing up and down and sailing in and out. They love the stormy salt spray, sun, fog, and smells of fish and sea foam. They love the way all of it's jumbled together; a sea chest of new and old adventures and discoveries.

It had certainly been an enchanted place for their family. The cottage had never been intended as somewhere for them to live. For one thing, it was small, and for another, they needed the rental income, and besides those things, their jobs and their lives were elsewhere. Windsong Cottage had been for them a haven, a getaway, an escape from the daily ordinary. And, as a place for family, the years they had spent there had given them a mixture of joy, adventure, struggle, and legacy.

Their own daughters had celebrated birthdays and graduations with a gaggle of girls through the years. There'd been scavenger hunts on the bay front while she and her husband drank coffee and "supervised." There were the girls' made-up ghost tours among the houses and through the shops of Nye Beach, the specters of those who had died in the collapse of an area known as Jump-off Joe always actively haunting the area—in spite of the fact that no one had been injured in the collapse.

They had ongoing adventures of discovering sea caves and new trails that meandered through the forest. There was the sheer joy of racing down sand dunes. There'd been one narrow escape when climbing the enormous boulders near Seal Rock while unaware that the tide was coming in. And there had been the almost tragedy of their youngest daughter being swept out to sea by a sneaker wave.

Her parents had stayed at the cottage for several weeks during her mother's battle with cancer. Mom and Dad had decided to revisit all the coastal places where they'd once gone deep-sea fishing together. They'd been so happy to have a home base where they could rest and still manage all the exertions of traveling from spot to spot in Mom's weakened state. On their final walk on the beach, they'd discovered the one glass Japanese float any of them had ever found. It now rested on the mantelpiece, a trophy to battles won and lost. It was a beautiful memorial and a conversation starter for friends who visited the cottage. Everyone wanted to know if it was real and how they had found it.

They had become closer as a couple through those years; young love gaining stability as their roots entwined and forged their way deeply into the soil of life. Their friendship had deepened as well.

126

Because, after all, this place was made for young lovers and families, but it was also made for friends.

This enchanted place where the coastal mountains greet the ocean shore was made for friendships…

They loved sharing Windsong Cottage with their friends. She'd been surprised by how the word had spread about their special place; from close friends to the friends of friends and beyond to visitors who came once and to those who returned again and again.

Friends came to Windsong Cottage for the Seaside SandFest, the Seafood and Wine Festival, Lincoln City's Finder's Keepers, the Kite Festival, and myriad other celebrations and festivals. And, of course, many others had come for long-anticipated seaside vacations. They came for the winter storms, and the summer sun, and the perfect temperatures of September and October. Whether they liked it or not, they also came for the rain that might accompany anything and anyone at any time.

One family had booked the cottage because their son was bringing his girlfriend along on this trip and he planned to propose to her. These friends of friends had been vacationing at Windsong Cottage since their boy had attended middle school. He wanted to ask the big question in a place where "so many other great things have happened." So one morning, during that stay, he had risen early and written, 'Will you marry me?' in the sand. He'd waited there beside his question for her to come outside before dropping to one knee to propose. His family had filmed it all from the cottage's upstairs balcony.

Friends had stayed after returning from long years of foreign missionary work, slowly acclimating back into the culture and ways of the US. Others stayed after a terrifying escape from Albania when the government suddenly expelled all NGOs from the country. Yet others had less dramatic escapes from their high-stress, hurried lives in the concrete jungles of New York City, Chicago, and Detroit. Still, others had found respite from the COVID lockdowns in Los Angeles.

There was the annual booking of the Red Hot Momma's Book Club and the Just Another Cuckoo Bird watching Group. Windsong had hosted Super Bowl gatherings, mushroom foragers, small church group retreats, knitting clubs, writers' groups, artists' groups, fishing buddies, and her favorite, Old Gals of Color. The gals were now septuagenarians who had been coming since they were all in their 40s. No matter who you were or what you longed to share, it seemed you could find a place within the Oregon Coast's patchwork of variegated harmony.

Right now though, she felt no connection or harmony. Today, she sought shelter here alone, returning to discover that this place was also made for the solitary and those who had lost their way. Like her.

This enchanted place where coastal mountains greet the ocean shore was made for the solitary and for those who've lost their way.

It had been years since she'd revisited Windsong Cottage. Somehow, in the crush of their daughters blossoming into young adults, and with their own demanding careers and the tug of other dreams, she'd stayed away. The cottage had mostly taken care of itself, aided by property managers who oversaw its cleaning and upkeep so others could continue to taste the coastal magic.

They had occasionally returned during their middle years with thoughts of selling Windsong Cottage since they lived so far away. Their daughters had been angry when they spoke of selling. And anyway, once they were here, there was always that spark of enchantment; of gravity pulling them together. Inevitably, they changed their minds about listing the cottage before returning to their other life.

Only once had Jack seemed insistent that they sell, and of course, all his reasons had been logical and valid.

"We never use it," he told her.
"The girls never come here," he reminded her.

He'd gone on that the place could use some major repairs and that they could use the funds elsewhere.

At that comment, she had quipped with all the whimsy she'd possessed in their early days, "I'll sell it only if you'll buy me another dream."

She remembered that searching look he had given her and the way they had both been silent for a long time. Then he had shaken his head and turned away. And the place where they'd once been young and in love faded yet again into the mists.

Now stepping inside, she breathed in the cedar fragrance and felt surprised the wooden siding still scented the home. Even in her sorrow, she sensed everything the cottage walls had enclosed through the passing years: the sighs of young sweethearts, the laughter of small children, growing families' excitement, squabbles and chaos, and good friends reconnecting—the benevolent phantoms of all who had sheltered here surrounded her.

She remembered some of the cottage's visitors. Remembered because—in the beginning—she and her husband had handled all renters. So many of them had returned year after year that they'd become friends of sorts.

The middle-aged man who booked all of January to write his book. Had he ever completed it?

She'd never asked.

There was a couple that booked all of February because they loved the winter storms. Had the wife passed away?

She thinks that was when their bookings stopped.

It seemed the widower had come alone that first year following his wife's death, but he couldn't bring himself to return again.

Had she sent a condolence card?

She couldn't remember, she'd become so busy. She hoped she'd taken the time for that small kindness.

They'd gradually lost all the personal connections as online booking and international marketing entities had taken over: Turnkey, Vacasa, VRBO, and AirBnB. And, honestly, they'd been relieved to let those personal connections slip away—as they had so many other connections to take their place.

Some of the cottage's visitors she remembered only from their comments in the guest books they'd always made available. There was the woman who claimed she saw a ghost in the upstairs bathroom.

"But don't worry," she had written as a P.S., "the ghost is entirely friendly."

"Oh, Casper!" Claire thought with a smile.

Predictably, others had picked up on the theme until there had been several "ghost sightings" in the upstairs bathroom. Reported ghost sightings had ended when a new guest book replaced the old. One guest's imagination played on another. This strange occurrence was acted out, again and again, in different themes throughout the years of guests with their imaginings and observations.

There was also the very strange visitor who had taken Scotch Tape and covered every knothole in the cedar siding and other imperfections on the beams and door moldings. It was such a strange thing to do that they had searched the guest book in vain to find an explanation. The action remained a mystery. The person had been so diligent in their taping that she'd bet that these many years later there was stray tape somewhere in the house.

But mostly she remembered Windsong Cottage visitors through their mundane and ordinary—yet still strangely endearing—messages:

'We loved being here; Thanks so much for sharing.'
'Beautiful spot; We will be back.'

'We loved spotting the whales from the deck. Thanks for having binoculars for us to use.'

Sometimes, a child would color a page with a picture of something they'd seen. Sometimes, kids used a few of the pages to play hangman. Those guest books held the messages of others who had loved and shared this place; treasures she hadn't bothered with in a very long time.

Looking through the misted windows to the sea, she shuddered, remembering her first glimpse of the view from this very spot.

How had she lost her way?
How had they lost their way?

They seemed solid enough for a while after the tragedy happened. Life had gone on, they had gone on, things had been fine…and then they weren't. Claire had no idea where to go from here, but she just knew somehow that back at Windsong was the place for her to be. She wrapped a soft blanket around herself and laid down on the bed they'd once shared, not willing to get under the covers. Lulled into a restful sleep by the music of the waves, she dreamed she heard echoes of long ago hammering from the years they had built their dreams together.

The new day brought with it fresh feelings of hope as if the ocean's horizon, which stretched on and on, held limitless potential that was still hers to capture. Even so, she hesitated. She'd planned to spend her time wandering the beach, but she couldn't endure even looking at the stairs that had once opened their lives to that stretch of sand they'd made their own. By late afternoon, she needed to escape.

Claire tossed a few things into her car and began driving up the coast towards Astoria; leaving the cottage and retracing the same steps her parents had so many years before. Crossing the beautiful bridge that spanned Yaquina Bay, she marveled that she could have neglected so much for so many years. Highway 101 trudged its way through the heart of Newport, Oregon, the cluttered commercialism of this main thoroughfare disguising all the treasures hidden in the bays, byways, nooks, and serendipity of the small, touristy town of 10,000 souls.

She passed the awe-inspiring Cape Foulweather, rising 500 feet above the Pacific Ocean where the rain-soaked Coastal Mountains jutted far out into the sea. It was the first point in Oregon that Captain Cook had spotted long ago in 1778. She drove past Otter Rock, Oregon's smallest Marine Reserve, and home to the famed Devil's Punch Bowl, then on through Depoe Bay, with the world's smallest, natural navigable harbor. The town was a wonderful display of nature's wonder to her left and charming storefronts to her right. She journeyed quickly past Gleneden Beach, where the ocean was invisible from the road, and entered the city limits of Lincoln City, once again sludging through another of Highway 101's stretches of cluttered commercialism. This city was home to 9,000 residents and 30,000 visitors each year, which illustrated all that the town offered beyond the main artery that wound through it. She was now midway between the equator and the North Pole. If only it was so easy to find your bearings in life.

She questioned the wisdom of revisiting the past, especially about going all the way back to her parents' past. But her parents had made a go of their marriage in spite of hardship. She remembered the way her father had wept at Mom's funeral. He'd been in love with her since they'd been in third grade, carving their names in a cottonwood tree, B.B. + D.F. when he was only 8 years old. But Claire and Jack had found their love later on, starting out with plenty of baggage to overcome in building a life together—and yet they had built a beautiful life. How could it be gone?

Traveling past Neskowin and Pacific City towards her parents' favorite deep-sea fishing ports of Garibaldi and Rockaway, she couldn't seem to avoid reflections on the past. But if she kept on driving, just driving on and on and on and on, could she find an entirely new future? Should she just drive on into the future rather than recapture the past? Without answers, she continued past classy, upscale Ocean City and then Seaside, Oregon, sometimes called the West Coast's answer to Coney Island.

On reaching Astoria, the northern end of the Oregon coast,

three things stopped her from crossing the bridge that spanned the Columbia River, where she could continue on until she found a new life.

One was the puzzling phone message from the property manager of the house beside Windsong Cottage:

"This is Heather from Home Sweet Home Vacations. We've had complaints about loud hammering noises coming from your property during the night. Please take steps to ensure that your guests respect the Lincoln County noise restrictions if you wish to avoid a formal complaint in the future."

The second was the sense that if she crossed the bridge and drove further away from her heart's anchor near Newport and their cottage, that something within her would break loose and tear and be irrevocably broken.

The third was exhaustion. She just couldn't do anything else right now except sleep. So she checked into a small B&B, climbed into bed, and dreamt of the life they'd shared until the smell of fresh coffee woke her in the morning.

Ugh. Rain and fog shrouded the day, obscuring the view in front of her. It was wet and oppressive and smelled of fish. Quite fitting for Astoria and nearby Fort Clatsop this time of year, she thought. But in spite of the weather, hope was surfacing within her. It bubbled up from that touch point between God and man; where inexplicable faith finds you and you know that all will be well. She had experienced it before. How apropos that she was here in this gloomy place unable to do anything really, but find her way home. This was the place where the famed Lewis and Clark had also prepared for their journey home. Of course, most of what she knew about their travels she had learned from Jack. Her husband loved to regale her with historical facts and the names of birds, trees, plants, and flowers. The Lewis and Clark Expedition was a favorite of his:

The travelers on that historic expedition would travel for more than two years, trekking 8,000 miles—most of it on foot—from the banks of the Missouri River to the Pacific Ocean. But in the rainy, windy, gloomy winter of 1805-1806, they had no alternative but to make a refuge here. It was a depressing, disheartening winter. In a 50-foot square fortification, 32 men, 1 woman, a baby, and a dog sheltered together. Many of them became sick and depressed while everything they had rotted in the rain. Though elk meat was plentiful, and the hides could provide them with coverings and moccasins, they had no salt so everything had putrefied. A search party eventually found a spot 15 miles from their fort to distill ocean water into the salt they couldn't survive without. It took everything they had to stay alive. From the beginning of November to the end of March—145 days—there were just 12 days without rain, only 6 of those clear. It was there that they prepared for their journey home. They had no real alternative, and neither did Claire.

Maybe the return home is the epicenter of everyone's journey; the focus of an earthquake and the center around which everything revolves. She only knew that she must find her way home again, whatever the cost.

Not all who are solitary find it oppressive.

They find solace in the sand and breeze, and the ocean's thunder. They find solace in the fellowship of books, brief conversations with strangers, the polite prattle of salespeople, and the pet that never fails to welcome them with joy.

But for her, she finds that she needs the partnership that was once theirs, the fellowship of adventure and folly that had defined them. She longs for the unpredictable safety of the life they had shared and lost. Home can be a person, a place, or a belief, but it is always an anchor that holds your position in a sometimes confusing world. Home keeps you from being lost in a vast sea. And so, at last, Claire discovered that this enchanted place is for the solitary and those who've lost their way, but it is also for those who must find their way home.

This enchanted pace where the coastal mountains greet the ocean shore was made for redemption and for finding your way home...

She pointed her car southward and headed back towards the anchor that was Windsong Cottage, contemplating how she could recover all that she had lost. For the moment, she had no inspiration or even a kernel of a plan. But she smiled with the knowledge that somehow it would happen. She knew it the same way she knew they would own the property and build their dream at the ocean's shore. She knew it as sure as she had written the word 'SOLD' in the grime and moss of the 'For Sale' sign the first day they had tromped through the brambles.

The mailbox with a colorful fish marked 'indsong Cottage,' the W long lost to some storm. It was difficult to find the driveway if you didn't know to watch for that. Claire and Jack had purposely cut the narrowest of access onto the property and through the brambles. They had built berms on both sides to buffer them from the sounds of busy Highway 101, covering them with plantings of ivy, shrubs, and hydrangeas. They left all the spruce and pine trees intact, in spite of the challenges they created during construction. The landscape was an oasis with lush vegetation, covering everything with greenery that created umbrellas over the walkways. From the decks that faced the ocean, you could spy just the beginning of the sheltered pathway towards the stairs—those magical stairs that led to their beach.

The cottage itself was built on piers to give them a better view of the sand and sea that stretched out across the horizon. It stood two floors high and outside, the cedar had greyed from the weather, becoming that special shade of silver caused by rainfall mingled with salt. The siding complemented the white trim of the windows and doorway and the cerulean blue of the doors. You needed to cross a wooden pathway and climb a flight of stairs to reach the front door that faced north towards the highway. A cheerful lifesaver buoy hung near the door, brightly painted with fish, and the words: 'Windsong Cottage'. The doormat bid you a welcome.

As Claire pulled into the driveway, she saw a note taped on the front door.

'PLEASE STOP HAMMERING AT NIGHT!!!'

It was written in large black, capital letters.

"What on earth?" she asked herself.

She circled the house before even going inside to unload her things, searching for any place where the siding may have come loose and started crashing in the wind. There was nothing. She circled again looking for shingles on the roof that could have detached, and then up above both balconies for anything that could be clattering in the wind. Nothing anywhere. There weren't even tree branches rubbing against the house. Claire found nothing that could disturb her neighbors.

Opening the door, Claire was instantly captured yet again by the unspeakably wonderful view of the ocean. Giant windows exposed the majesty of a crashing, frothy, unending sea. She found herself catching her breath once again at the sight. The deck that stretched beyond the entire south face of the house extended the panorama. It was from this deck that the stairs lead to the pathway that brings you to the stairway, down to the ocean. But the only part of that wonder that you can view from the deck is the opening in the trees.

She still loved the warm, caramel patina of the cedar walls as they contrasted with the white vaulted ceilings that were echoed by the timbered beams. She still loved the white tile interspersed with orange, yellow, and blue-tiled fish that decorated the kitchen and bathrooms. She still loved the blue, white, and yellow décor, those colors and the ocean theme that caused the house to come alive with cozy comfort. The cottage could use some updates, but she'll never change the color pallet, or curtain the windows.

Claire settled in for the night, climbing the stairs to their one-time bedroom. She stood briefly at the upper balcony facing the sea.

"How many people have watched the sunset from here?" she wondered.

Then she settled into bed and read herself to sleep, the light from the moon and the sound of the waves a slumber-inducing wonder. That night she dreamed they were building again, the hammering of construction mingled with her dreams and she woke unsure of what was real and what wasn't. If the noises weren't part of her dreams, then something really was pounding in the night.

The next morning, coffee in hand, she headed to the deck to enjoy the horizon and contemplate how to spend the day. She began sorting through blankets and dishware and removing faded pictures and decorator pillows, piling them by the door to cart off to Goodwill. The beach continued calling her, but she couldn't yet bring herself to weave through the path to their stairway—to walk again on their beach. Instead, she took possibly the biggest and most illogical risk of her life. She wrote a note and put it in an empty bottle of Bordeaux, corked it tightly, drove to the next beach access, and tossed it into the sea.

The message says only: Jack, Please find your way home. Claire.

The ocean currents caught the bottle, but it never traveled out to sea. The wind and waves carried it south only until a visitor enjoying the tidal pools of Seal Rock rescued it.

Claire continued driving south. She passed the coastal community of Seal Rock, its name taken from the large offshore rock formations that are home to seals, sea lions, sea birds, and other marine life. She made it across the bridge that spans the Alsea Bay, beneath which lies the water that's home to thousands of Dungeness crab, clams, salmon, and steelhead, and arrived in Waldport before needing another stop for coffee. Then she journeyed through beautiful Yachats, the Gem of the Oregon Coast, and on past Cape Perpetua—a favorite haunt of theirs where she couldn't bear to stop.

Highway 101 South took her past the trails they'd hiked up and across to Heceta Head, and to the Hobbit Trail that leads down to the ocean. She pulled into the viewpoint to gaze at the Heceta Head Lighthouse as if she were a tourist. There were eleven original lighthouses once protecting sailors from this dangerous coastline. They had been spaced about 30 miles apart, so no one would be lost on the violent cliffs and shoals. She found that knowledge oddly comforting.

Claire continued on, passing the famous, and famously smelly, Sea Lion Caves. The cave is America's largest sea cave and a year-round home of the Steller sea lion. The tourist spot had been in operation since 1932, and she had no idea how many times they'd visited. As she traveled further away from Windsong Cottage, Claire knew she would soon turn back. Once she had reached Florence, Oregon, the beautiful bridge across the Suislaw River would bar her way as surely as the bridge in Astoria across the Columbia River had stopped her—though after Florence there was another 130 miles left of the Oregon Coastline. She walked a bit through Old Town Florence, lost in memories and lost in time, before getting back into her car to drive back.

Everything pointed her toward home.

Claire returned to find another note from her neighbors taped to the door.

'Please stop with the nighttime hammering!'

There was also a letter in her mailbox from Home Sweet Home Vacations with a noise violation complaint. Angry neighbors surround her. Again, she checked for some source of any hammering sound; a loose board, a shingle, or a tree branch, but found nothing. So, for another night she read herself to sleep and dreamed once more that they were young and in love and building the cottage together.

The morning of the big event was misty and cold, with just a hint of sunshine sending glimmers across the ocean. The mingled fragrance of coffee and cedar scented the air. Whales were already spouting, so in her slippers and sweats, she went out on the deck with binoculars to get a better view. And there, at the bottom of the deck's stairway, was the bottle she'd cast to sea, holding wildflowers of purple and gold. Claire picked up the bottle in wonder, looking all around her for some clue as to how it got there, before heading back inside to place it gently on the table.

After that, she tried every contact she had for Jack: Email. Text. Voicemail. Screams. She tried again, and again, and again. But there was no response.

That night Claire had no intention of sleeping. She wouldn't let herself sleep—in spite of the fact that she was one of the world's best sleepers. One cup of coffee after another helped as she paced the floor waiting for time to pass. And time did pass, as it always did. The sun set, the moon rose, and a light mist softened the sky. It was dark outside now. Claire wrapped herself in a blanket and sat on the deck listening, trying to discover if the hammering sounds were real or phantoms of the past just visiting her dreams.

At first, she heard muffled sounds, like boards being shifted or scraped against rock.

But soon there followed a *thunk, thunk, thunk,* a pause, then *thunk, thunk, thunk* yet again.

Outside as she was now, Claire judged the sound was loud enough to wake anyone trying to sleep outdoors, but not as loud as she'd expected based on the angry complaints. Still, there was a fair amount of noise, and it was coming from the direction of the beach. From her vantage point, Claire could easily see the path that led to the stairway they'd built so long ago—their access to another world. Then the hammering paused, and she almost turned away. She almost let the moment pass, afraid of what she'd find.

But hadn't she already allowed too much to pass?
Stopped taking any real risks?
Become too focused and drab?

She grabbed a flashlight and headed off the deck and through the trees towards their stairway to the beach.

And there was Jack.

The thing about their stairway was that it really was just an ordinary structure of wood and nails built over the sea grasses covering the cliff that it traversed. But the access it gave them had always seemed magical to her. The point of being so near to the ocean, she had always believed, was being able to get close and touch it. Just looking was never enough. They had built stairs from their property down only as far as the top of the large boulders that acted as a buffer, protecting the bank from being washed away and carrying the cottage out to sea. It had always been a bit of a climb over those rocks and down the rest of the way, but they'd never minded until age began to creep up on them. Jack appeared to be building the rest of the stairway, from the top of the boulders down to the sand.

"Hey," he greeted her.

"Hey yourself," she'd answered.

Then he looked up at her, hammer in hand, smile on his face, and said, "We need to finish this."

And she had smiled back. Because she knew he was talking about more than the stairs.

"You're going to have to stop hammering in the middle of the night," she told him. "The neighbors are having fits."

"Tonight is all I need," he responded. "If you'll help out and hand me the nails."

So they had completed their stairway as the rain misted over them, the night waned, and the day began breaking. Back inside the cottage that morning, they had clinked their coffee cups together and solemnly promised that they would never bother the neighbors again.

"How did you find the bottle?" she asked him.

"I didn't," he said, "The bottle found me. But I was already here, Claire. It was the oddest thing really. I started camping on the beach near Seal Rock about the same time you arrived. I could see lights in the cottage, so I guessed you had come here, too. Anyway, one evening just before I headed over to work on the stairs, this guy walked up to my tent with a bottle in his hand. He asked me if my name was Jack, and when I told him it was, he said, 'Jack, you need to go home.' Then he handed me the bottle with your note inside and walked away"

"Quite serendipitous," she laughed.

"Quite," he replied.

After that, they began to rebuild all that had fallen into disrepair, both at Windsong Cottage and in their lives together. Because, how could they just walk away from all of their history, let it be washed away like the sandcastles they'd built on the beach? How could they turn their backs on those heartfelt vows they had made to each other, just let them crumble into the ocean like the resorts once built on the cliffs of Jump-off Joe? And how could they face the future with any kind of excitement and confidence if they couldn't build on and learn from all that had been between them? They had built a good life, and they were determined to clear out the brambles that had grown up to choke it.

Jack and Claire focused mostly on the future, treating gently any wounds from the past, offering and receiving forgiveness, and feeling their way forward together. They spent time talking and listening, allowing friendly silences to fill the spaces in between. They revisited all the old places they'd once loved, finding adventures again in the trails and beaches, the bays and rivers, the book shops, antique stores, and eateries. They visited the coast's festivals and fairs, took road trips, and watched all the old movies they'd once loved. Together, they made a very long list of all the new things they wanted to try— their future was a vital counterpoint to their history.

The coastal weather was a constant reminder to them that not every moment can be filled with sunshine. Even so, the intermittent storms and clouds and wind made the sun's warming rays even more welcome; and so it was with Jack and Claire as they found their way past all that had been broken and began to build again.

They made plans to add on, enclosing the area under the pillars to make room for a fireplace, and to have enough space for family and friends to stay with them. The cottage was to be their home. They agreed to add a gazebo to house a hot tub and an outdoor barbecue; put in a secret garden, and a fire pit, and an outside shower just big enough to rinse the sand from their feet.

One day as they talked about the changes they were making, she said to him, "We're not getting any younger, you know."

"Yes," he replied. "I'm pretty sure I understand the way that works."

"Well, I think we should make all these additions and changes to the cottage in such a way that we can easily turn it back into a vacation spot whenever we want," she told him.

"Why would we do that?" he asked.

"Because," she said, "We've always loved sharing this place, and I've always wanted to travel the world."

"Not sure I follow you," he replied.

"Others can rent the cottage and use it while we're away. Our place will never get lonely. And no matter how long we travel or how far away we go, we can always come home and pick up where we left off. Does that make any sense to you?" she asked him with a twinkle in her eye.

"Very little," he replied, kissing her on the forehead and smiling into her eyes. "Let's do it."

So she knew for certain that everything between them would be okay. Because when it came right down to it, this enchanted place where the coastal mountains greet the ocean shore was made to hold not just the past, but also the future. It was a place to journey from and back to again and again.

D.C. Chester

By L.W. Smolen

Up in the Oregon Coast's mountains, there are lost little cemeteries and graves – a lot of them – lost, forgotten way up in forested, nowhere places like Ten Mile, Death Ridge, Desolation Saddle – places nobody knows – except Loggers – where probably living Loggers buried Loggers mashed by logs.

Since I got served, I seek those cemeteries, because there, I don't have to talk to anybody. Days, at work, I stumble along. Nights, I just wander dark streets crying. I seek lost cemeteries because everything there is the truth – birth, death, the creaky old grave markers. In those remote cemeteries, nobody is screwing with me. Good places to get away from life. Besides, the Fall rain brings with it Halloween.

On a Friday, I was at work when the Sheriff served me the papers. My wife is suing me for divorce, taking everything. I'm telling you – the knucklehead shit you pull on someone to whom you've proclaimed love catches up!

When I got home, the house was empty – of her, of our four-year-old son – but full – of hot hell-heat. So much heat, it got me sweating before I had everything shut off. Every light on, the furnace turned all the way up, every burner on the stove glowing bright red – even the flopped-open super-over-heated oven – the washer, the dryer, the TV, the stereo repeating over and over again Donovan's "Season of the Witch". And up in the master bath – her stupid, plug-in, helmet-hair curler set – hot – and, too, the cranked-up-full space heater in there – all of it burn-down-the-house hot! The whole house like full blast ninety inside. The wallpaper cooked. It really shook me all up. But it wasn't like her.

I told Dick, my Lawyer, whose pointed nose and short legs reminded me of a Dachshund, how it all felt – the Sheriff at the office – the crematorium house. Dick said he knew Mildred's Lawyer, somebody named Graydon Jensen. Dick described him as "just a crummy flat-lander" from over in Eugene – and that the ruthless terms of the divorce suit were "right up the guy's alley," probably instigated by Jensen himself.

Then Dick said, "You don't know it yet, Joe, but you hired a gut-fighter, and we're going to a formal hearing!"

*   *   *

Just a week since I got served, I called in sick. It's raining and I can't face this second Friday because a realtor who uses a black cigarette holder with pearl inlays is showing our house today. But for me, it's the Chitwood Cemetery. I've been there one other time in twenty years. Nearly forgot about it. You get it just off Highway 20, up the Yaquina River, just east of the covered, artifact Chitwood Bridge. A bit of barbed wire fence is all that encircles the collection of jumbled graves. Years ago, a big windfallen hemlock crushed the whole north section of the fence.

People worry about logging and things like habitat and the carbon cycle, but the jungle of the western woods will always reclaim everything; it's reclaiming the Chitwood Cemetery.

Rain. I tell myself I don't need any rain gear. Won't take long.

The rusted hinges of Chitwood's cold livestock gate stop me. I realize with a kind of shock, how much the western woods' jungle thickens in just twenty years, how much I wish I had brought along my machete.

The first trespasser in years and years, I lean against the steel gate. The rusted hinges break loose. I force in. Instantly, the tall, wet grass soaks cold right through my Levi's to the skin of both my shins.

Face-to-face with the soggy tanga-tanga of vine maple, huckleberry, and salal, I stumble and try to step over a big moss-covered log, but my left foot drops into space. As I fall leftways, all the clinging rainwater hanging in the jungle canopy above me pours down

144

my neck.

I can't move. My left leg, clear to the hip, is stuck straight down in a rotting pit between the log I tried to step over and a tangled root-ball. I breathe. I feel my lungs being invaded by the acrid stink of rot and infecting clouds of fungal spores. The Chitwood cemetery. Everybody there is dead.

High above me in the trees, a slap of rain squalls in with our first October storm.

My left leg stuck down in that hole, a giant, four-foot-tall sword fern bushes right in my face. My right hand grabs onto a bunch of the cold, wet blades, and hard as I can, I haul myself up onto my right knee and pull my left leg out of the hole. I end up in the exact same position as an altar boy at Mass – bent at the waist, my face a foot from the first grave marker I spot – it lying flat.

Looking down at it close-up, I see the marker is hand-knapped out of a piece of the dark grey basalt of the Pacific Northwest. Cheap, common rock, but way back in 1938, somebody chiseled out the initials "M.E.F.", and below the death date, "Feller". I can't tell if Feller is a last name or the job he was doing when he got killed.
I'm already soaked. I start to chill.

I spot a concrete headstone shoved over to the right like sixty degrees out of the vertical by a spruce maybe thirty years old. Leaning against the cement headstone's front like it was used as a vase five years ago, stands – I can see a child leaving it – a little, screw-top Starbucks bottle.

My whole grave crawl goes that way: I find eighteen. But then I start to really shiver in the wet. Up in the trees above me now, the power of the wind is a constant, loud rush and clunk of trunks and branches. I think about the forty, fifty-year-old hemlock that blew down a long time ago and flattened the north section of the cemetery fence. I could get myself chilled and killed both, right here in Chitwood Cemetery. She'd get everything – probably even my Social Security. Deserves it.

I need to get out of here.

But I don't.

What do I really have to lose? Lightening-strike Mildred is at last divorcing me.

And when I see the level spot and the dinky, cast-iron fence and the carpet of little spring-green, two-inch-tall plants – each with a single, sweet little heart-shaped leaf – when I see the rusted, long ago love-lavish of the little fence...

There are actual flowers carved into the little diaper-white marble headstone. There are actual little five-petaled pink flowers growing in amongst the tiny green hearts. The plot isn't over four feet square. I can still read the date easily – in detail – "August 19th, 1914". Only that one date. I realize with a thud that, oh man! It's a little baby's grave – born/died same day. It makes sense – except...over and over, I keep reading it. The initials don't really work on a newborn's grave. The little headstone reads "D.C. Chester."

All I can figure is, what the hell kind of a parent could've been so coldly impersonal as to cap off such wrenching, sudden loss – the loss of their little, bald-headed baby and its tiny little pink fingertips that never lived long enough to even get sucked on - with just initials? I spend another hour systematically combing the Chitwood Cemetery. I don't find anybody else with the last name Chester buried there. I feel slightly better. D.C. Chester. At least D.C.'s mother survived the birth. Her poor little baby's death was heartbreaking enough! It's cold enough. I'm cold enough. To hell with it. I get out of there and I limp back to a cold, empty, Friday night house.

And I just step out of a hot shower when the realtor calls. How soon can I move out? When can I sign the Earnest Money? I can hear it in his voice – the way he talks – teeth clenched on his mother-of-pearl-in-laid black cigarette holder and chrome-grinning like the grill work on a '56 Oldsmobile. Standing there, damp towel over my shoulders, I'm getting chilled again. I feel bad for poor baby D.C. Chester again.

He shows up in thirty-seven minutes – the in-laid cigarette holder does. I sign away our house. The realtor exits. I have thirty days to get out. I shiver. I feel like hell. I get myself a beer. I hammer it down.

I obsess over Chitwood Cemetery. Burping beer, I think about all those neglected graves. I puzzle. I head-butt the everlasting mystery of D.C. Chester. During my second beer, I get really frustrated and pad barefoot into the bathroom to drain my lizard. Sudden anger bursts up and I kick at her little embossed, underwater-scene, tin garbage can under the bathroom sink. Instead, my foot hits the edge of the bathroom door - which rattles stupidly on its hinge pins and my big toe starts to bleed and my red blood gets to staining the white grout on the tiled floor, and on my hands and knees, I use beer and my dirty underwear and tears of frustration and heartbreak to clean up the blood. I tape up my toe. I cry myself to sleep.

*   *   *

By my second Saturday morning, all I have left in the world is coffee. I shod myself. I'm going. I'm getting out of here – out of this sold damn house. It's not our house anymore, anyhow.

I can start packing tomorrow or the next day or the next week as far as it goes.

Thinking about really good coffee, I feel my heart take a little leap of relief. I'll even get to feel fifty-cent magnanimous and tip the kids working there. I jump back in my van and feeling really pretty hopeful, I drive to Newport to a place called Panini, my coffee fave. Like usual, it smells wonderful in there, and the heat of the all-night-long baking that goes on in the back keeps it homey warm. I hug my molasses-thick Sumatra and let the warmth and the personalness of Panini osmose through my skin. Perfect coffee again. Perfect heat again. Ahhh.

Many times, I've studied the cedar-shingled buildings out Panini's front windows across the street. Once more, I marvel to myself that the shingle installer screwed up right there at the front door. The building is really quite nicely trimmed-out turn-of-the-century style – pale green, fluted side-casing on the front door – wide, crowned casing over the top – but all the shingle courses are about an inch lower to the right of the front door than the left.

I know that mistake; my own shingle courses had been out by the same amount and where it showed was right smack at the front door!

And so – I'm steeping in Panini's warmth and I'm sipping my perfect coffee and I'm commiserating with the long gone installer's downer when suddenly, D.C. Chester is back and for a moment, I think about that little cast-iron-fenced plot again and all I feel is oh, good grief! Do I really have to go over it all again? Now? I actually think it – that D.C. Chester is nothing but a cat-in-the-hat joke. But D.C. Chester was a name carved into a tiny white headstone, set in a cemetery plot, fenced in ornate cast-iron. How could such a life be a joke?

Worse, when I'd arrived at Panini, I hadn't had the sense to power-off my phone and it rings right in my perfect coffee. It's the realtor. He wants to know who D.C. Chester is. He says that's how I signed the Earnest Money Agreement. He's pretty jacked. He's actually yelling. He can really sympathize with my divorcing-me wife. I find myself smiling and hoping, as I talk to him, the smile isn't coming through in my voice. It's ridiculous. All of it. Just stupid. I tell him I'll be at the house in ten minutes; wanting to get him over with, I do it in eight.

After we get the Earnest Money Agreement all squared away, I sit there in the house just smiling at the realtor, him scowling and frowning over his delayed commission and stuffing another cig into his holder.

"What are you smirking about, Joe?" he wants to know. "Ree-ahl-tee," he insists, "It's called Ree-ahl-tee because it's REAL!"

Then, he puffs a cloud and asks me how I feel. It's a shock that he'd even ask. I want to know why. He says, "You look like shit. You must feel like shit."

148

I know I deserve some abuse. I'd been self-absorbed. When we got married, I told Millie I was writing a novel. Like it was equivalent, she said, "I have Eczema." She accepted my novel.

She said, "Take ten years and see where it goes." At nine years, it hadn't – gone - and I was desperate to produce more income than my part-time liquor store job, and behind her back, I'd day-traded Millie's astute, shell-game household savings and I didn't pay attention and I lost it all. I'd been sloppy and careless with the Earnest Money Agreement, too.

I realize with a stab the realtor isn't really the jerk. I am.

But I digress. I don't care. I don't care if the deal gets to Closing or not. I don't care what my angry, divorcing-me wife thinks. I don't care what anybody thinks. All I can think about is everlasting D.C. Chester. D.C. Chester. D.C. Chester. I realize with a kind of crazy elation right in that moment that I'm gripped by D.C. Chester – just like the obsession I once had, Millie or not, of owning a chick-magnet sports car. I loved my wife. She and I stuck together like magnets. It wasn't the chicks. It was the stupid car I wanted – bad.

And we bought it and one day, driving by myself on Highway 34, in a hairpin turn up on the east side of Mary's Peak, the back end of my red sports car passed me and I stuffed the beautiful front end into a dirt bank. The other side of the road was a canyon. That car was a widow-maker. Probably should have, but she never made me eat any crow at all.

*   *   *

Two weeks after Millie leaves me, I just can't stand it anymore. Back at my Panini sanctuary, right from my perfect coffee, before my mind starts sniffing the D.C. Chester trail again, I try once more to call my wife. This time, she makes the mistake of picking up.
"Millie?" I say.
"Wut?"
"I need help, Millie."
"I know. So get some."

"Millie? I've been spending too much time in cemeteries. I feel nuts."

"At least you're planning ahead THERE."

"Millie?"

"Wut?"

I don't dare tell her how I really feel. She doesn't owe me anything. Instead, I start to blabber. I describe the whole scene at Chitwood. I tell her about D.C. Chester. I tell her it's nuts, but that I can't stop thinking about it, that I'm researching it, but getting nowhere. She just lets some exasperated steam out her ears like she does and tells me in her practical voice, "Oh, Joe. Somebody from the Siletz Res probably just buried their dog in there as a joke." I say back that she wouldn't think so if she could see the place – the tipped-over headstones, the underbrush.

I tell Millie I love her. I say I've been a fool and I'm sorry as hell and that the house sold already. She just says, "I know."
Then, recklessly, I ask her to "please" meet me at the Chitwood Cemetery. I say, "Remember the red sports car and how it got ahold of me and I nearly got killed? This D.C. Chester's got me the same." I tell her where the cemetery is and ask her if ten is OK. Over the phone, I can tell she's crying. It's exactly like when I was a kid when just looking and listening around, I figured out that once you get involved with a girl there'll be a lot of crying. Back in the 6th Grade, though, I just never figured I'd be the cause.

She doesn't say no to Chitwood. She doesn't say anything at all. She just snuffles and I think I can hear a cough drop clicking on her teeth as her tongue shifts it around. Probably, she caught a cold since she left me; it tells me how stressed she is. Over the phone, in the background, I hear a scrap of our son's voice. We'd worked hard for that kid. Something was wrong with my output, so we really worked hard to get Millie pregnant – if you can call obsessive-compulsive sometimes-nearly-public sex work.

Listening to Millie snuffle over the phone, I feel like a creep. Our separation is real rough on her.

She never says another word. She just hangs up.

150

The only place Millie shows up is about a month later at Gut-fighter Dick's formal hearing. By then, I'm out of the house and basically living in my rusted-out seventy-three Ford van. It wasn't mentioned in the papers the Sheriff served me. It's only worth about two hundred bucks – but it'd been handy – back in our really-wanna-get-Millie-pregnant days. It's real tough, sleeping again in that tin can without her wrapped around me.

But the hearing.

I show up, too, but I can't really even focus on the proceedings. During the month, I researched D.C. Chester at the Lincoln County Historical Society, the Newport Historical Society, the Waldport Historical Museum. I have a scratched-off list of a hundred key-word combinations I Googled. Odd thing I ran across was a full-blood Salish from clear up in northern Washington somewhere who used to live in Chitwood way back. I couldn't figure out if his name was Smack Billy or that's just what people called him. The reason it stuck in my mind was what Millie had said once about how the justice of the Indian-land casinos and somebody from the Res burying a dog in a white man's cemetery as a joke were the same thing.

Which brings this confounded story back around to Millie. At the hearing, it's real obvious she's over her cold. She glows. She looks so hot in a tight gold on black she hasn't worn in ten years. That outfit isn't about cleavage; it's about her erectness; the high Manchu collar lifts her tractor-beam persona up on top of a tower.

And she has her dancing violet eyes all sparkled up so bright, she has her own Counsel all screwed up and in his opening arguments, he loses track of what he's trying to say and has to go back to the table where Millie's sitting and check his notes and when he does, he makes the mistake of looking in her eyes again and he flusters and drops his notes on the courtroom floor among the chairs and there's a glass of water on the table and that falls, too, and gets his notes all wet and – well - the whole thing just carves my guts out, because it's was so killingly obvious to me how easy it had been for Millie to replace me.

Millie had unbolted me from herself like a bad-order starter motor nicking up the teeth of the flywheel of her super-charged, big-block, V-8 girlness that long time ago she had used to pull me off my foundation. I'm scrap metal to her now.

In the courtroom, I can't stand that she never looks at me once, so I watch her lawyer. Even red-faced from embarrassment and bending after his dropped notes, he's magnificent: tall, chiseled, tailored suit a color nobody could name, but even I can tell, perfectly matches his super-healthy skin tone. Anybody can see Graydon Jensen's a full partner in his Firm.

But Dick's exactly what he called himself. When Jensen fumbles his papers, Dick tears right at Jensen's throat. Dick jumps up, requests "respectfully" to be allowed to "approach the bench" where I can just barely hear him start in on some deal about a mistrial on account of the prosecuting attorney's "apparent lack of familiarity with the facts in the 'Mildred vs Joe case'", and how Dick can't stand to let his fine client be "fired from the Philharmonic of his life" over "notes he didn't even drop."

No kidding. Dick says that. I see the Judge's eyes twinkle.

But which only gives Jensen a chance to recover himself and so our two lawyers go at it, and yakityak yak yak, and in the middle of a hot legalese exchange, Dick just turns away from Jensen, and about me, he says directly to the Judge, "Look at my client, your Honor. Just look at him!"

That's when I realize that, for the first time during that entire hearing, Millie's eyes are on me.

We always could. Millie and I always could look fearlessly at each other – I mean, not staring – just gazing – I mean, speaking at least for myself. Millie is more like a Sphinx – always making me wonder what the hell a girl like her is doing with me.

Like the first time we had sex. At first, we just laid there on her bed in her apartment in our clothes – I guess, gazing. A few minutes later, in the middle of it, I asked her directly, "What are we doing? Just getting our share?" The way she answered, I was never the same. From way down in her chest, she just said, "Oh, how can you even say that!" There during that trial, facing the sphinx again, I remember that whole thing and realize with another saw-cut downbeat, that after all the years, I don't really understand Millie one bit.

She just sphinxes me for about two minutes and then she uses her eyes to beckon Jensen. She takes ahold of the lapel of his tailored suit pulls his face real close to hers whispers something in his left ear – or maybe kisses it – I can't tell. With a smug, satisfied look, Jensen just stands up and requests a "lunch recess". It's early, so the Judge gives us a coupla hours. Jensen shuffles my life back into his briefcase. Then, Jensen and Millie stand up and leave – just like a couple.

Outside, right away, in a fit of depression, I nearly get hit by a bus. Only reason I don't is it was really trucking and I felt it shake the street and I looked up in time.

Coupla blocks away, I find a dive bar called the "Wishing Well". It's before-lunch-empty - just me and the tatt-necked bartender - who says, "Hi. My mom calls me 'The-odor', but I go by Toxic Teddy." For myself, I say, "Hi, I'm - 'In-Need-of-Whiskey'." Toxic Teddy says he has "a supply of that". Toxic Teddy still has a jukebox, too – with nothing on it but Fleetwood Mac, and "Gold Dust Woman" forces me to think about Millie's gypsy magic – the magic she'll never ever again work on me.

I get back to the Courtroom early. Dick the gut-fighter is ahead of me. Pacing fast, back and forth, like a caged wolf I once saw alongside a highway in Arizona, he grabs the cuff of his right jacket sleeve with his left hand and yanks, snapping the sleeve straight. Fast, he does the same with his right hand. He repeats. He just paces and yanks. Paces and yanks.

There's going to be blood on the courtroom floor, and I'm tanked up enough to be seeing two gut-fighters.

Watching the Dicks, I begin to fear they'll get ruthless and pull some muddy personal stuff on Millie. I have to admit, though, I didn't oppose very hard, but I never did want to go to formal hearing – for Millie's sake – but then I'd remembered the hell-heat in the house, and the lop-sided terms of the summons I'd been served, and I re-realized that I was the possessor of faulty judgment and decided to just 'let 'er rip' – as my dad would've said.

The hearing wraps up quick.

Millie comes back through the courtroom's double doors all by herself. I expected and looked, but no Jensen. From up in her tower, she swings into the court room not looking at anyone. She sort of curtsies to Dick and smiles at him. Then, she walks straight over to me, and clutches at my right hand, but misses and stumbles and almost falls off her high heels. She looks in my face and I don't know what she's seeing, but I see only anguish in hers. On the second try, she gets my hand and says, "Let's get out of here, Joe."

Outside, her only comment is, "I suppose you parked the van your usual mile away." Besides walk fast, the only thing she does is squeeze my hand like she wants it to graft onto hers.

It wasn't a mile. Sometimes Millie exaggerates. I'd parked in one of those spots that's right at the outbound end of a busy bus stop and I guess there was some kind of bus service interruption because there were about twenty impatient people bunched right there close and stupidly fiddling with their smartphones and re-touching their make-up or trying to read or escape conversations absolute strangers are victimizing them with.

I let Millie in on the curbside. I go around, but by the time I get in, Millie's on the other side of the green and white-striped curtain that I have hung behind the two front bucket seats.

She's out of her gold-on-black.

I see a meteorite shower. I see planets and galaxies. And somewhere in what Millie does to me next, I hear a coupla buses thunder in and take the world away. Somewhere else, I get all stupid bold and I ask her the same question I had so many years before. Millie answers different. She says after I'd invested twenty thousand bucks without telling her and then never paid any attention and lost it all, she was really mad and I say, "Yeah. I got that." Thoughtfully, she traces my lips with a fingertip and she says back, "So I decided I had to blow the lid off everything and see where it all landed and find out all over again how I felt."

I don't ask Millie any more questions. I can feel how Millie feels. Even obtuse me. I can tell.

We just lay there for a while, listening to passing downtown traffic and more buses booming in and blasting off from our van's back bumper. Out on the sidewalk, a loud guy tells whoever's out there that, "The wind might be alive!"

To Millie and me, the familiar patterned rust on the sheet-metal ceiling of our van is like constellations in a starry starry night sky we'd watched a lotta times years before, and laying there right in the middle of downtown, we find out we both remember it – real well - all of it. But then, Millie jumps up, yanks on my sweats. She bends over and kisses me in her tender way. Last, she pokes me in the chest with a finger and tells me, "Chitwood Cemetery. Midnight." Then, though, she seems to re-think. Two-handed, she cradles my face and her eyes search mine. From down in her chest, she adds, "Trust me."
She leaves me her gold-on-black.

*   *   *

When the Highway 20 bypass was finally completed, the section of coast highway past the Chitwood Cemetery was abandoned. Now, it's a closed-casket-dark midnight along the road at deserted Chitwood. No traffic. There're no houses or lights – no Millie – nothing near where I know I'll have to climb the bank from the highway and find the cemetery gate. A ground fog a coupla feet deep muffles the stillness.

That's when, suddenly, I see a white phantom appear from the other side of the empty highway, float across the pavement, and ascend the bank just about where I'm expecting to find the cemetery gate.

Ridiculous. But the apparition shakes me. I shiver.

As I approach the gate, inside my skin, I jump when from directly on my right in the dark, I hear Millie say, "There he is, Danny. Your dad!" and all I can think is, "Good God. Now she's involving our innocent son. But then, I remember her 'Trust me'."

The white ghost from the road reappears and floats toward me. latches onto my right leg and hugs it hard. Then, the little goblin giggles and tells me, "We're tricking." Danny talks like his mouth is full. I can smell chocolate.

Millie comes up and kisses me and says, "OK, Joe. Can you find the grave?"

I know what she means.

Millie has an LED headlamp for each of us. She takes Danny by the hand and he giggles again. A few steps inside the gate, we lamp up. Millie smells like chocolate, too.

But it's inky out and the bright LED light bounces off the ground fog and right back in our faces. Because of the big sword fern I'd mangled before, it's easy to find the hole my left leg went down into and I show Millie "M.E.F." chiseled in block lettering. With a chuckle in her voice, she tells Danny, "We already got our candy from everybody earlier, but we still get to trick. Are you ready, hon'?

He wants to know what the trick is. His mother just says, "Trust me." Then she asks him if he's having fun and he says, "Mommy, I'm stuck!" and she hands me a short – shovel! - she's carrying, and picks Danny up and tells him, "Almost there, hon'" But me! Millie and I lived Dracula. Only a coupla months after I read the novel, and felt the dread in Doctor Van Helsing's "Mein Gott!", I woke up on a warm, windows-open summer night, to hear the exact same Castle Dracula bat-wing-fluttering sound right in our own bedroom. I freaked. No question what it was. We listened to the Count circle around our dark room. After I dithered a while, Millie just got up and caught the bat with her bathrobe.

So now, I'm in a burial ground with my wife who I now know I don't know near as well as I thought and she has just handed me a shovel. Mein Gott!

But I'm in no position to tell Millie anything.

Then, Danny wants to know if we're at "daddy's house." Millie pipes one of her short, high-pitched laughs and answers, "Ha! You're pretty smart!"

Danny giggles again and says, "We're going to pull a trick on Daddy, aren't we."

Millie just says, "If you weren't a ghost right now, you'd get a big kiss from me."

Scares me, the way I feel my heart hammer. Hefting the shovel, I bend and reach down through the ground fog with my other hand and find the little cast iron fence. All I can think is Mein Gott! What have I done?

When I just stand there paralyzed, Millie gets impatient and yanks up two sections of the little cast iron fence. She takes the shovel from me. She starts to dig. While she's digging, she asks Danny if he remembers what a skull is. He giggles and raps his own head with the knuckles of his right hand and says, "Dad told me what a knucklehead is." And then, out from under his white ghost costume, he produces his own little spade. Millie says, "Let's find one."

Their shovels chuff, chuff, chuffing, I realize they're actually exhuming poor little baby D.C. Chester.

Just like in the courtroom, it's over quick. The grave is shallow. I hear Millie's shovel clunk and Danny exclaim, "Mommy! Big te-e-e-th!" Millie adds, "And what big eyes this cat's got to see you with!" I see Millie pull a plastic bag out of somewhere and reach down into the dark hole, lift something out, place it in the bag, and start to scrape the dirt back into the hole. She hands me back the shovel and replaces the little fence and just like at the hearing, she says, "Let's get out of here." Then with a smile in her voice, she tells Danny, "A trick isn't a very good trick if you get caught, though, is it."

So we turn out our LEDs and I hear Millie whisper to Danny about how we should stay and stand still a few minutes so we'll be able to see in the dark and nobody will see us and he asks, "Like ghosts?" and she says "Yes."

But after only about five minutes of standing there, out of nowhere, he says, "Mommy. I gotta drain my lizard."

Millie absolutely hates that phrase. She had. She'd tried on several occasions to save Danny from me and lizards. But when I hear it in my own little son's voice right then, right there – just like an audio lighthouse - in the blackness of that lost, forlorn cemetery, I can't stop my throat from suddenly closing up. I feel my eyes flood hot – and sting. It's all so obvious to me in that gold-on-black moment, that Millie will never be able to differentiate Danny from me, nor me from herself.

We just stand there, a family, in that absolute blackness, and listen to our little son whizz in the brush.

*   *   *

Six months later, we bought a dinky, six-hundred-square-foot house in Newport up on Lucky Gap above Agate Beach. D.C. Chester's skull is back where it belongs. Turned out, way back when I called her from Panini, Millie pretty much knew what D.C. was. You probably figured out I'm still trying to write.

You probably figured out, too, that Millie found out something more about D.C. Chester. She said she talked it around over on the Siletz Reservation. Millie talks to people, but they have no idea how she's listening. She'd make a hot-shot homicide detective. Somehow, what gets said to Millie chunks into little logical slots in her mind, and when something is said that doesn't fit, it sticks out and she asks more questions.

Over in Siletz, on the Res, she started out telling them about people her parents knew over on the other side of the state at the

Warm Springs Res. She told them what she found in the Chitwood Cemetery. In the Siletz Tribal Office, they listened to her and they finally started talking. Millie said that sure, they knew the name Smack Billy, but when she tried to dig, their faces got flat and they said, "If you really want to know, come to the Siletz Pow Wow next Summer. Don't ask who you're talking to. Just ask about Smack Billy." That's as far as she got.

*   *   *

The following year, by the time we drive over to Siletz to the Pow Wow, Millie's huge pregnant again. It doesn't take Millie long before she spots the same woman who she had talked to at the Tribal Office the previous fall. The woman motions reluctantly in a general direction and says, "Go to the cemetery. It's over there on Government Hill. Someone will meet you."

At the cemetery, waiting quite a while, we don't see anyone, but we feel watched. Then, a wraith of a dark old woman not over five feet tall, her long black hair heavily greyed is just – there. We don't see where she comes from. Instantly, we know not to ask her name. The front of her ball cap is white. All in big rainbow-colored cartoon lettering, her hat yells, "YEAH!

After she studies us coupla minutes, she just shrugs and tells us, "My great-grandfather abandoned Puget Sound when the Seattle died. Not long after he got here, everybody was herded onto this reservation. But Smack Billy and his pet bobcat were renegades like Paulina. But, when Chester died, he came back here."

Last, the old woman steps back into the brush behind her and is gone. But not before I read on the back of her t-shirt, "It's Supposed to Hurt."

Frustrated, we want more. We sit on a bench and wait, but nobody else comes. We walk back to the Pow Wow, but Millie won't quit. Even though she's due in only a month, she leaves me and Danny, and he and I shop the vendors and eat. Danny and I watching the drummers, I see a coupla more copies of the old woman's t-shirt walk by.

Coupla hours later, Millie's back. Walking down the hill, back to the car, she tells me, "When I ask around about D.C. Chester, they just smile. She tried to dodge me, but I told the woman at the Tribal Office I was having contractions. She was so sweet to me! I didn't even have to ask. In a back room, where there was a couch, she admitted, 'The story goes that, smiling, Smack Billy buried Chester at Chitwood, and then about a month later, he disappeared forever – from right in front of his great granddaughter's eyes.'"

I listen to Millie, but all I can think to reply is, "Huh?"

But then, I ask Millie what Smack Billy's joke was - exactly.

Like I said, in Millie's mind, things chunk into logical slots. She just looks at me, rolls her eyes, and lets some exasperated steam out of her ears like she does, and then ...well, you know how you might be standing real early on a fresh Summer morning by a big, still pond? And way out in the horizontal sun that glows on the glassy water, you spot a little, lone ripple? And you know it's a fish just lazing? Just touching the surface with its back? And your wondering mind fastens to the mysterious bigness of the fish? That's what I see Millie's promise do – just bump the surface of her face and, she kisses me.

Whale of a Christmas Crime

By Valerie Davisson

Ramona stomped her feet on the mat and hurried inside. They had enough propane for a few more days, but they'd need to get the tank refilled soon. Shrugging off her coat, she hung it on a peg inside the door of the tiny travel trailer she and Gordie called home. Everything inside was so small; it was like living in a doll house a child had outgrown and thrown away. Still, even a rusted roof over your head was better than none. Thanks to the steam coming off a large, dented pot simmering on the two-burner cooktop, at least it was warm. A single sink with two feet of counter space between it and a minifridge constituted the rest of the kitchen.

To the right of the fridge was a compact nook with built-in, facing benches. A drop-down board served as their dining table. Tonight, it was set with two deep soup bowls, two spoons, and a plate in the middle with sliced radishes, lime wedges, cilantro, and avocado. It wasn't fancy but it was the best she could do given their current circumstances.

Picking up a wooden spoon, she lifted the lid of the pot. Clouds of steam warmed her face, frizzing the front of her hair. Tender, spicy meatballs, fat with rice, floated in a rich broth alongside big chunks of carrots and potatoes. She closed her eyes and breathed in the rich, complex aromas. Albondigas con caldo always reminded her of home and family. Tonight, she was counting on it triggering those feelings in Gordie, too.

Normally, she cooked up at the big house, but the old man was getting crazier, and she was getting tired of dealing with his ludicrous fantasies. What Charlie needed was family; someone to come and take charge and take care of him—that's what families were for. But if he had any, they never came to visit, and he'd never mentioned siblings or a wife or children. Other than a picture of his parents above the fireplace in the dining room, who surely must have passed away by now, they had never seen any other evidence of relatives.

Gordie was more patient with Charlie than she was. Tonight, Gordie was up in the 'Cinema Viewing Room,' watching an old movie with Charlie, but he assured her he would be home in time for dinner. Charlie always fell asleep halfway through the film.

She didn't want to be unkind, but this could not go on forever. Charlie needed help. She knew it, even if Gordie didn't. Or didn't want to face it. Gordie had always been too kind.

She smiled.

They'd met at her cousin's quinceañera in Los Banos, California. When her brother's car broke down, Gordie didn't hesitate to come pick them up, even though Salinas was an hour out of his way. Sitting between the two young men on the bench seat, she snuck glances at Gordie all the way home. Being only 5' 5", Ramona usually just came up to a guy's shoulders, but Gordie was barely taller than she was. She liked being able to look him in the eye when he turned to smile at her now and then.

Later, as they spent more time together, she also got a kick out of having to translate for him. Gordie's grandparents came from Mexico, but when they arrived in America, they insisted their children only speak English at home. As a result, Gordie looked Mexican, but didn't speak a word of Spanish. At least he was Catholic. Her parents would never have let her go out with him if he weren't.

Gordie's abuelos established a small, family farm in the Salinas Valley. She and Gordie were married in that farmhouse. They thought they'd live there forever, raising children, working the land, but life had other plans. The large commercial operations gobbled up one family farm after another. They held out for a long time, but even putting in fourteen-hour days to keep things going, they couldn't outwork a three-year drought. Every year they got deeper into debt. Eventually, AMINC, one of the largest agricultural conglomerates in the area, paid pennies on the dollar for the house and land. And just like that, they were farm workers, not farm owners.

Her brother offered to take them in, but she knew that would kill Gordie. He may have lost his farm, but he still had his pride.

162

They sold everything that wouldn't fit in the truck and headed north to Oregon to join the thousands of other migrant workers who flocked to the orchards to pick fruit.

Rubbing the small of her back, she sighed. Even after Gordie hurt his leg and couldn't finish out the apple season, her husband still thought he could someday buy their farm back. Ramona was under no such illusions. By now, AMINC had probably knocked down the house and outbuildings to make way for soybeans or almonds.

An old woman suggested they try their luck on the Oregon coast. Winters were milder than in the valley and there were places to camp off the highway if you followed old logging roads. Plus, there were jobs to be had on fishing boats. That was the plan, anyway, but the truck had broken down at the end of what they thought was a logging road.

It turned out to be the road to Charlie's place. The light from his house was the only thing they could see through the trees. They were lucky he'd taken them in and offered them work. Gordie would never have lasted on a boat, even if he'd managed to get himself hired. Gordie got seasick in the shower.

Ramona needed to cheer herself up. Tonight was October 31, the beginning of Día de los Muertos, her favorite holiday.

At home, Day of the Dead celebrations lasted three days, filled with fun and family, cleaning gravestones, sharing stories, and reconnecting. Family was everything. Here, there was no family to visit, alive or dead. And they lived too far from town to have made many friends here yet. In fact, they rarely left the ranch. It wasn't a ranch, really—that's just what Charlie called it. He referred to the rambling house and outbuildings as La Cuesta Encantada, The Enchanted Hill.

It was beautiful here and in the right light, set against the trees, the old house did look enchanted, but...

Ramona shook her head and got back to reality, surveying her preparations for tonight.

163

In spite of the high cost of everything here on the Oregon Coast, she had managed to scrape together enough money for a small ofrenda or altar, which she'd set up on an orange crate next to the door, where they could see it while they ate. It was nothing like the ones her family had made back in Salinas for the holiday, but on it she had placed bright yellow-orange marigolds, two pieces of pan de muerto, a sweet bread, and in the center, a bottle of tequila for Gordie. She hadn't been able to find any brightly-colored sugar skulls, so she'd picked up a bag of hard candy at the dollar store in Newport and placed that in a bowl. It would have to do.

It was Halloween here, of course. America had different traditions. She knew about trick-or-treating, but she was pretty sure no kids would make it this far back in the forest. The road was steep and unpaved. No one ever came here. Still, she would share the candy if any brave child made it this far.

Giving the soup one last stir, she replaced the lid. She was hungry but sat down to wait for Gordie.

Sometime later, Ramona jerked her head up off the table. She blinked her eyes several times before making sense of the noise that had woken her up. Relief flooded through her as she realized it was just her husband knocking the mud off his boots before coming inside. Nervous, she finger-combed her hair away from her face and pinched her cheeks, looking anxiously toward the door. She would feed him first, then deliver the news.

Chapter 2

NOVEMBER 1

Logan tried not to be a pig, but Anna and Ken's smoked salmon was sooooo good! Not only did they smoke it themselves, but they caught it up in Alaska, where they cruised around every summer, returning to their home in Little Whale Cove in Depoe Bay each fall.

Introduced by a mutual acquaintance to Anna and Ken a few months ago, the two couples hit it off right away. They had enjoyed several dinners together, since. Ben, of course, cooked when Anna and Ken came over. Logan had no problem with that. She was not known for her culinary skills. Ben was definitely the chef in the family.

Forcing herself to slow down, Logan surreptitiously stabbed a few more pieces of smoked salmon with her toothpick before filling the rest of her hors d'oevres plate with crackers and olives. She was definitely going to have to unbutton her jeans, and they hadn't even gotten to the main course, Anna's lasagna, or dessert. Brownies topped with vanilla bean ice cream and caramel sauce. OMG.

They were seated at the bar in the kitchen, watching Anna wrap the garlic bread in foil and put the salad on the table. They visited while Anna continued to buzz around the kitchen. "How did your witch thing go last night?" Logan asked, referring to the annual food pantry fundraiser Anna and Ken participated in every Halloween. "What's it called again?" "The Witches of Depoe Bay," Anna said, tapping the screen on her phone, handing it to Logan. "Here, swipe right and you'll see Ken in all his warlock glory!"

The first picture was of Anna and several friends dressed in long, black witches' gowns and pointy hats, dwarfed by her six-foot-two husband, also in black, sporting a scarlet-lined cape, topped by a neon green fright wig. All of them waved signs and held out sacks and boxes to accept food and cash donations for the local food bank from people as they drove by and waved. Everyone looked like they were having a great time. "Green's definitely your color, Ken!" Logan said, going through all the pictures before handing the phone back. "How much do you guys collect on these drives?"

Anna checked the lasagna before shutting the oven door. "We still need to count up what the Newport and Chester's groups got, but we had a good haul this year!"

"That's great!" Logan said.

"Still, there are more and more homeless every year; we need every bit of what people can give. Oh, thank you for the donation from your foundation, by the way."

Although Logan no longer worked full-time with Fractals, a math/music education foundation she'd started a few years ago, she still signed off on grants and donations and this one was a worthy cause. Still, she wished there was more she could do.

She shared her thoughts with Anna, who promised to let them know about upcoming volunteer opportunities.

"Be careful what you wish for, Logan! I'll have you signed up for every bake sale and cleanup project from here to Alaska!"

Logan swallowed and wondered what she'd gotten herself into. Volunteering meant making commitments and giving up some of her independence and free time. She'd just gotten some white space on her calendar—always a treasured commodity. She loved having the freedom to run on the beach, play her violin, Bella, compose music, or just sit on the back deck and listen to the forest when she felt like it. But she and Ben had talked about wanting to get to know their neighbors and serve in the community, so she gamely smiled and reaffirmed her offer. She could always say no later.

For the rest of the night, Ken ran through his and Anna's Alaska slideshow and regaled them with tales of close encounters with grizzlies and orcas. It all looked amazing. They even took their German shepherd, Misty, on their adventures every year. Misty was quite the sailor, although not a big fan of the long truck and ferry ride to get to the boat.

Speaking of Misty, she had fallen asleep on the couch, her head resting on Ben's lap. Watching them, Logan felt a stab in her gut. Two years ago, Ben had lost his dog, Purgatory, a greater Swiss mountain dog he'd raised from a puppy. Purgatory was named for his love of— and gastric reaction to—Polish sausages. Almost fourteen years old, he had been slowing down, but losing him had still come as a shock. One night, he curled up in his dog bed as usual, only this time he didn't wake up.

Last year, Logan thought she had found just the right dog for Ben, a two-year-old labraheeler named Dixon, a rescue from the local animal shelter, but it soon became obvious the dog had bonded with Logan more than Ben. He joined her on her morning runs and kept her in sight at all times around the house, following her from room to room. The rare times she actually sat down, Dixon would lay at her feet. In fact, usually on top of one of her feet, so as to make sure his mistress didn't get away. Ben had been a good sport about it, but he still didn't have a dog.

Watching Ben run his hand gently down Misty's head and side made Logan's heart hurt for him. In all the years she'd known him, Ben had always had the faithful Purgatory at his side. He even took him to work in his truck on landscaping jobs in Southern California where they had lived prior to moving to Oregon. Ben's nephew had taken over the landscaping business and bought Ben's house, so Ben was kind of at loose ends up here in more ways than one.

Logan had her music, but once they finished fixing up the house, Ben needed a new passion, or at least a project, until he figured out what he wanted to do.

Chapter 3

NOVEMBER 2

Logan refilled her coffee mug and settled herself in front of the fire. She flipped open her computer to check her email and send Anna a thank you note for last night's delicious dinner.

Ben had gone into Salem to get snow chains—it rarely snowed on the coast, but some of the passes driving inland or to the airport required them. Who knew? He was also making a Costco run, but said he'd be back before dark. The house was quiet without him.

Scrolling through her inbox, deleting junk emails as she went, she almost missed one from Anna. The woman hadn't wasted any time taking her up on her offer to volunteer the next time something came up.

Hi Logan (and Ben),

If you'll be back from California by Nov 25th, come to our annual Wreath Making Party! Good way to meet people. 4:00 p.m. Our garage. I'll have all the supplies and gear, just bring yourselves and thick gloves if you have some. If not, don't worry—someone always has an extra pair.

It's slave labor—but you will be paid in pizza and beer. Hope you can make it. We need all the hands we can get. We have a couple of days to finish them, but they need to be hung along the bridge in time for the tree lighting on December 2. Call me if you have any questions!

Logan and Ben were going back to Jasper, CA for Thanksgiving, would be back Friday, so barring delayed or canceled flights, they should be home in time.

Crafting wasn't Logan's thing, but she could load a glue gun, cut cedar boughs, or attach wire hangers to the backs. If nothing else, she'd volunteer to pick up the pizza or make a beer run. Before she could change her mind, she hit reply and, with full disclosure of her limited artistic skills, said they'd be there. Satisfied, she hit send. They'd been forewarned.

She took another sip of coffee, then pulled up her calendar, added the wreath-making party, and double-checked their airline reservations for Thanksgiving. So far, everything looked good to go. Next, she logged onto Amazon and searched for gifts for five-year-olds.

The last time she'd seen him, her grandson, Ian, was big into owls, but who knew what he was into now? She'd have Amy or Liam send her some links for things he might like. She would have some toys shipped and wrap them when she got there.

They were doing Christmas with the kids early because Liam's folks, who lived in Scotland, were flying the family over for the whole month of December. Occasionally, Logan felt a small twinge of jealousy and competition with the other set of grandparents. She and Ben ere comfortable, but Liam's folks were Old World wealthy.

Landed gentry from where that sort of thing counted. Barons or Lords or something, she never could keep European titles straight.

Scooting a little closer to the fireplace, Logan warmed her hands on her mug, grateful to be snug and warm. This must be how early humans felt, tucked into their caves, safe from sabretooth tigers and howling snowstorms, warming themselves around the fire.

She loved their new house. Well, new to her and Ben, anyway. After sitting vacant for a couple of years, it had taken a lot of elbow grease to whip the place into shape, but it had been worth it. The old girl had good bones. Wide-planked hardwood floors that softly glowed in the firelight, generous rooms, large, solid windows. On the west, the house faced the ocean, which was down the hill and across Highway 101 to Depoe Bay.

Even on days like this, Logan left the windows open a crack so she could hear the fog buoy, the seagulls, and during storms, the pounding waves. To the left of the fireplace on the back side of the house, the view was all trees. Cedars, mostly, with shore pines and alders mixed in. She and Ben often sat on the deck out back, breathing in the sharp, fresh smells of the mixed conifer forest. It was her go-to place for thinking and composing.

When she'd done the initial walk-through of the house, it had boasted only a horrific smell of raccoon urine and mice droppings, but Logan wasn't one to give up. With the help of a local miracle-worker handyman named Clay, she and Ben had scrubbed and repaired and painted the place into a home that would last for years.

She drank the last of her coffee. As the caffeine began to clear her brain, a musical phrase that had floated in and out of her consciousness the last few days started taking shape. She reached for Bella, her violin, which she kept hanging on the wall nearby. Handed down from her father, the beautiful instrument had been lovingly made for her Appalachian great-grandmother, Norah, by the love of her life, Giovanni, a talented, young Italian immigrant.

After playing around with the notes, Logan recorded the phrase on her phone for later retrieval. Later tonight she'd see how it fit into the larger composition she'd been working on.

Right now, even though Logan was tempted to hunker down with another cup of coffee and gaze dreamily out through the rain-splattered windows, she needed to get her butt in gear. She'd promised Sam she'd help her out with a special project this morning. Sam hadn't said what the project was, just to be at the newspaper office first thing. The NewsTimes opened at 10:00 a.m. If she hustled, she'd have time to pick up some donuts on the way. She assumed any self-respecting newspaper office had copious amounts of coffee.

Chapter 4

NOVEMBER 2

Sam met her in the lobby and walked Logan back into the bowels of the newspaper production area, stopping at the bottom of a rickety, metal staircase that led up to a precarious, suspended platform that ran along one wall, far above the printing press.

Logan involuntarily shivered. There was no way this was up to code.

Sam, completely unconcerned for her own or Logan's safety, scampered up the stairs to a long, rectangular table where several large binders were already stacked and waiting. She pulled out a chair and sat, pointing to one opposite for Logan.

"Welcome to 'the Morgue!'" she announced with a sweeping gesture, pushing her trademark hot pink, rhinestone-encrusted, cat-eye glasses up her nose.

Logan looked around.

Running along each wall in open shelves were rows of black and dark blue binders, labeled Newport News, News Media, or simply NewsTimes, most with a range of years handwritten on the spines. Some looked very old and worn.

Sam explained that this was where physical back issues of the bi-weekly newspaper were stored, going back to the 1880s. Whenever she wasn't out reporting on current news, Sam liked to comb through these looking for stories that got dropped, interesting locals to follow up on, or start writing obituaries on prominent citizens who hadn't died yet.

Logan hadn't thought about it, but it made sense to prepare obits in advance so they could be written in a timely manner when someone actually kicked the bucket. Made her wonder what someone would write about her. Food for thought.

Sam already had them set up with two tall thermoses of hot coffee, but they had to keep them on the floor between their chairs. After inhaling a couple of donuts each, they wiped their hands off thoroughly before handling the binders.

Starting around 1930, the plan was to work their way forward, looking for interesting people who may still be alive to write about. There were a few old codgers over a hundred years old, but probably not many.

Logan was soon lost in the annals of local history. Some of the pictures showed nothing but trees and a couple of tents where the town was now. In an hour, she was up to the 1950s. "Here's someone interesting," she said. "Betty Taunton . . . Says she came here in 1951 to run the Spouting Horn . . . that's the same place as the Horn in town, right? Maybe she's still alive. She'd be in her nineties or so, though."

"Good call," Sam said, "but we just did an obit on her. She died in August at the age of 93. She was known as the pie lady. Keep digging!"

Disappointed her work hadn't yet yielded any leads to living people, Logan kept skimming. By noon she still only had a few possibilities for Sam to follow up on—an ambassador at the end of a successful career with postings from Rome to Greece who'd planned on retiring in the area with his wife and son and opening an art museum downtown with some of the classical pieces from their private collection, a story about an independent fisherwoman named Molly McCullough with a successful business and a somewhat shady past up in Astoria, and one about a logger who had raised an orphaned black bear from a cub.

Sam said the ambassador and his family must have retired somewhere else because she'd never heard of them and there was no art museum in town, but she'd check on the fisherwoman and the logger to see if either was still alive. People loved bear stories and fallen women who beat the odds were always inspiring and fun to write about.

Logan let Sam treat her to lunch at the Horn. If indulging her nosy nature included free food every time, she'd be happy to help Sam whenever she wanted.

They grabbed an upstairs table near the window and lifted a glass to all the colorful characters the Oregon coast produced and attracted. After lunch, Sam checked in with her editor, while Logan enjoyed the view. This morning's sky had been a wet, steely gray, but while she and Sam were digging through dusty newspapers in the morgue, the sun had banished the clouds and sprinkled diamonds all across the harbor. She could feel the warmth of the sun's rays through the glass.

Before moving here, all she'd heard about Oregon were jokes about the weather, like "Oregonians don't tan, they rust." The spectacular sun breaks were a well-kept secret.

When Sam left to interview a city council member before tonight's meeting regarding a proposed redesign of a stretch of highway in downtown Newport, Logan decided to take advantage of the sunshine to play tourist and walk off lunch.

Crossing Highway 101 at the light just outside the Horn, she tried the whale-watching center, but it was closed Mondays and Tuesdays, so she sat on the observation bench just outside for a while. Most gray whales had already migrated to Baja to have their calves, but every year a few stayed behind. She heard a familiar whoosh as one of the resident whales spouted water no more than a few yards away from the rocks. She watched as the gentle giant cruised by, exposing its mottled, barnacle-scarred back, then sunk silently below the water before surfacing again halfway across the harbor. She never tired of watching them.

The sun break was brief. As the wind kicked up and the clouds snuck back in, Logan decided to get moving. She hustled along the seawall down to the whale statue, a familiar Depoe Bay landmark. Someone had told her the artist had done their research and the sculpture was the actual size and shape of a real gray whale calf, about fifteen feet long. If that was the case, Mama Gray must have been huge!

Logan could have walked home from here—their house was only a few streets up and over, but she'd left her car at the Horn, so she pulled up her hood and hurried back, making only one stop for two bags of caramel corn at Ainslee's. Tonight was movie night.

The whole downtown was only four or five blocks long, ending in the stone bridge which spanned the entrance to Depoe Bay harbor, the smallest harbor in the world—or so they claimed. This was the area Anna and Ken helped decorate for Christmas. And this year, she and Ben would be helping.

Logan turned on her windshield wipers and reached into Ben's bag for a handful of warm caramel corn. He'd never know.

Chapter 5

As they turned into the entrance to Little Whale Cove, Logan smiled. It was official. She and Ben were an old married couple. It was Saturday night and their big date was going to a wreath-making party in someone's garage.

When they got to Anna and Ken's, they parked across the street and walked down the steep driveway. People were already bustling around the brightly lit interior, setting things up.

"Hi! Glad you could make it!" Anna said, coming out to greet them.

Oohing and ahhing over Ben's artfully arranged, gourmet cheese tray, Anna led them back to the food table. Ben was very popular at parties. Logan followed with a six-pack of IPA. After putting the beer into a red and white cooler anchoring the end of the table, Logan looked back at the offerings on display. Lusting after a plate of chocolate chip cookies and a bowl of Reese's peanut butter cups, she wondered if anyone would notice if she slipped a few into her pocket to hold her over until the pizza got here.

Before she could decide, Anna hollered up the stairs to let Ken know they had arrived and steered them over to two long worktables edged with folding chairs, piled in the middle with evergreen boughs. The sharp, fresh scent of cedar put Logan instantly into the holiday spirit.

Several people had already begun working. An attractive woman with long, silver hair looked up from fluffing out a huge, red velvet bow. Deftly adding a wire tie with a single twist, she tossed it into a box and said hello, while reaching for more ribbon to make another one. She'd clearly done this before.

Anna assigned Ben to cedar bough fetching and trimming, and stationed Logan at the end of the assembly line, two chairs down from the bow lady, with needle-nosed pliers and a roll of wire. Relieved she was not going to be expected to master bow making, Logan got to work. Wreath hangers she could handle. More people arrived and soon the small garage was buzzing with energy as supplies and gossip were passed back and forth and old friends caught up. Logan was happy to let the cheerful blend of Christmas carols and conversation swirl around her. Most of the people there were part of a core group of volunteers who helped organize and run other Depoe Bay annual events like the wooden boat show, the Witches' food drive, and the salmon bake. Most were retirees, but not all. One family had three generations at the table: grandma, dad, and two teenagers. The mom would have been there, but she had the flu.

Logan wished her family could be here, but Amy, Liam, and Ian were leaving for Scotland soon and her brother, Rick, only got a few days off work. At least she and Ben had been able to spend Thanksgiving with everyone before they scattered.

Logan had even been able to fit in a short visit with her old neighbor, Lori, while Ben helped his nephew put in a new garbage disposal at his old house. Calvin was doing great with the landscaping business but was new to home ownership and still had a lot to learn.

At around nine o'clock, things started to wind down. Four satisfying stacks of completed wreaths waited to be loaded into the back of Ken's truck. Several people said they would meet at the bridge at one o'clock tomorrow afternoon to hang the wreaths. Ken and his two-man crew would be done hanging the candy cane and whale decorations by then.

Leftover ribbon and cedar branches were given to anyone who wanted to take some home, along with any food. Except for a few stray bits of cheese and sliced black olives, the Tidepool Pizza boxes were empty, and thanks to Logan and the bow lady (a new friend) nothing chocolate had survived.

Logan and Ben stayed to help with cleanup, but even then, they were home by ten. Because she hadn't worn the work gloves Anna had so wisely provided, Logan spent a good twenty minutes attempting to scrub tree sap off her fingers. Soap and water didn't touch it and picking at it only succeeded in getting it under her nails. Ben just shook his head and came back with some rubbing alcohol. It came right off. Was there anything this man didn't know how to do?

Heart full of gratitude and good deeds, Logan pulled him into the bedroom to sample her husband's other skills.

Chapter 6

NOVEMBER 26

Logan pressed the cold soles of her feet up against Ben's warm body and burrowed deeper into the covers. It was still dark outside, and they didn't have to be down at the bridge until 1:00 to help hang the wreaths.

Sundays were for sleeping in. Or at least they were before they got a gray and black fuzzy alarm clock last year. Dixon, their labraheeler rescue dog, gave another sharp bark and waited expectantly at Logan's side of the bed, wagging his tail, waiting for his morning run.

There was a price to be paid for true love. Groaning, she reached for her sweats.

Three miles and forty-five minutes later, Logan got Dixon his breakfast and let him out on the back deck, then went to get back in bed with Ben. She kicked off her shoes and got under the covers. Snuggling into a comfy spooning position, she allowed herself to drift back to sleep. Her plan was to stay in bed until she smelled bacon and coffee.

In what could only have been two seconds later, she was blasted awake by the not-so-dulcet sounds of the Boogie Woogie Bugle Boy of Company B.

She really needed to change that ringtone.

Finding her phone on the nightstand, she tapped the screen and mumbled a grumpy "Hello?"

"Logan, it's me, Anna."

Before Logan could form a sentence, Anna continued, "I hate to bother you, but I need your help."

"Okay," Logan said, almost awake now, "Sure—shoot." "After you guys left last night, Ken went up in the attic to pull down the candy cane and whale decorations. He was stacking them by the door so they'd be easy to load in Bill's van this morning."

Logan nodded, then realizing this was a phone call, not a video chat, she said, "Okay," and waited for Anna to get to the point. She remembered vaguely that Bill was part of the crew that helped Ken mount the wooden decorations up along the downtown section of Highway 101 in Depoe Bay.

"There are about thirty wooden decorations to put up down-town—ten whales and twenty candy canes. The last few years, Ken, Bill, and Mosley have been able to get them all up in a couple of hours. Ken contracted with Central Lincoln—the power company—to use their poles."

Logan swung her legs out of bed and pushed her feet into her Uggs sheepskin slippers. Ben got up to make coffee.

"That was the plan this year, too. Bill was supposed to pick Ken up this morning in his van at 8:30 a.m., swing by and get Mosley, and then have all the whale and candy cane decora- tions up before lunch. Then we'd meet you guys and the other volunteers down at the bridge to hang the wreaths."

Anna took a big breath, "But, last night Ken took a header off the ladder trying to get up to the attic—he should have waited for Bill, the man has no patience. The bottom line is we spent most of the night in the ER down in Newport."

"Oh my god, is he okay?" Logan asked, following Ben into the kitchen.

"He will be, but he busted his ankle in two places," she said. "It's a bad break. The doctor said he's grounded for the foreseeable future. I just put him to bed with a pain pill."

"What can we do to help?" Logan asked, nodding at Ben who'd just put the coffee on.

"That's why I'm calling," Anna said. "I hate to ask such a big favor, but could Ben help the guys get those decorations up this morning? Everything's ready; it should only take a couple of hours. But if he can't do it, don't worry, I have other people I can call."

"No, of course," Logan said, looking at Ben, who nodded yes. "We'd be happy to help. Do you want him to come there?" Anna let out a big sigh, "Yes, thank you so much! I'll call Bill, but I'm sure as long as you're here by nine, you'll have plenty of time to get everything done. I usually go along to lend a hand, but I need to stay here with Ken. He has allergies and doesn't always do well with pain meds." Logan said she'd take Anna's place and keep her posted throughout the morning.

She and Ben were breakfasted, showered, and parked across from Ken and Anna's driveway just as a tall, dark-haired man who must be Bill opened the doors of an old minivan. He had removed the third row of seats to make room for the tools he used for his handyman business. They helped him load the signs in the back, then got into the middle seats, leaving shotgun for the rounder, shorter Mosely.

Anna handed a thermos of coffee through the window as Bill put the van in gear to back up out of the driveway.

"Let us know if you need anything from the store or pharmacy," Logan said. "Do you want us to bring you back some lunch? Thai? Mexican?"

"No, we're fine," Anna said. "I've got stuff in the freezer. Thanks so much for doing this for us."

"Just wait 'til you get our bill," Logan laughed. "Sundays are double overtime!" she added, waggling her coffee thermos as Bill pulled away from the house.

*****

The sun had been up for an hour already, but the streets were still deserted. Downtown shops didn't open until eleven on Sundays, so they wouldn't have any trouble finding a parking spot.

"Let's start at the north end and work our way back to the bridge," Bill said as he pulled into one of the spaces facing the bay. While the guys wrestled with the ladder, Logan got one of the candy cane decorations and started carrying it over to the first pole.

As she approached the end of the sidewalk, she stopped. Something didn't look right. Her brain tried to make sense of what was different when it suddenly clicked.

"What in the . . . ?"

She blinked and looked again. Nope. It wasn't a trick of the light. The life size sculpture of the baby gray whale she had admired yesterday, its tail rising playfully in the air, was gone.

Chapter 7

Bill was right behind her on the front end of the ladder he and Ben were carrying. It was clear by the look on both their faces that they shared Logan's shock. Mosely brought up the rear with the toolbox.

They all stood around staring at the empty cement ring and pedestal that used to support a sculpture of a baby gray whale, metaphorically scratching their heads. For a long minute, nobody could think of anything to say.

Finally, Logan said, "Maybe they took it down for repairs or something."

"Nah," Mosely said, "I would have heard." Mosely worked for the city and with Depoe Bay being so small, he would know if the mayor ordered a box of paper clips, let alone the repair of a life-size baby whale.

"Besides," Ben added, echoing everyone's next thought, "they wouldn't take it down right before Christmas. Isn't this where the tree lighting ceremony's going to be in a few days?"

"Yep," Bill said. "Tree lighting's this Saturday. Wherever it is, they'd better get it back by then."

Logan thought of college pranks where seniors stole the rival team's bulldog or toilet-papered the dean's house, but this wasn't a college campus, and the whale wasn't a mascot of any athletic team or fraternity.

"Who in the world would want to steal a whale statue?" Logan said.

Having exhausted all the options they could think of, Bill did the practical thing and called the non-urgent number for the Newport Police Department. Dispatch referred the call to the sheriff's department. A full-time position for a sheriff's deputy had recently been approved, but that person was not on board yet, so the sheriff said he'd send one of his patrol deputies out as soon as possible. He collected their phone numbers in case they had to leave the scene before he could get someone there. "As soon as possible" turned out to be an hour and a half.

Long before law enforcement arrived, the press did. In spite of being a busy mother of an eight-month-old baby, Sam was tuned into her police scanner twenty-four-seven. If she could have managed it, the scanner would have been surgically implanted. "So," Sam said, pushing up her glasses as she got out of her car. "I hear there's a whale missing?"

Logan filled her in then waited while she asked the guys if they had anything to add. Just as they were wrapping up, the sheriff's deputy arrived. He asked the same questions, but no one knew anything, so he said he'd file a report and got back in his car.

When Sam left to write up her story, Bill decided there was nothing more they could do, so they might as well mount the candy cane and whale decorations, grab a bite to eat, and then meet the rest of the volunteers at one o'clock to hang the wreaths along the bridge as originally planned. At least one part of Depoe Bay would look Christmassy.

Chapter 8

They decided on the Sea Hag for lunch. Once the waiter dropped off their drinks and left with their orders, the conversation turned back to the subject of the missing statue.

"Not a college prank," Ben said. "I agree."

"Could still be high school or college-age kids—or anyone under the age of twenty-five who had one too many at the Horn," Bill said. "Kids don't need a logical reason to do some- thing crazy that sounds like fun."

"It's not some priceless work of art like Venus de Milo," Ben said. "What would be the motive?"

"Why would someone want a whale statue and where would they put it?" Logan asked.

"I'd put it in my backyard. Let the kids play on it," said Mosely.

"Nah, if it was me, I'd steal Venus. I'd definitely take a naked woman in my backyard over a whale, and I wouldn't let the kids anywhere near it!"

"Well, whoever took it must be crazy," Bill said. "And we've got no shortage of crazy around here."

"Did I ever tell you about my Uncle Joe?" Mosely asked. "He was sharp as a tack until his wife died, then he started talking to the toaster.

Thought it was Aunt Shirley."

Bill took a swig of his beer.

"Swear to god!" said Mosely, holding up his right hand, palm out, in testimony, the very picture of innocence.

Before Bill could argue, the waiter brought their burgers and for the next few minutes, everyone focused on the food.

Munching thoughtfully on her cheeseburger, Logan looked out the window at the ocean and thought about who could have taken the whale statue and why. Something was niggling in the back of her brain, but she couldn't quite make the connection between her subconscious and her hamster-wheel thoughts.

She tried free-association. babies—mothers, whales—ocean, sculptures—statues, Venus de Milo—ancient Greece, art— museums . . .

Bingo!

Logan swallowed her last bite, then put her burger down, and reached for her phone. It was a long shot, but possible. She needed to get back into the Morgue at the NewsTimes to see if her idea made any sense. Sam texted back right away and told her she could meet her at the paper in the morning after her sitter got to the house to watch the baby.

Logan sat back in her chair. Now that she had a lead to follow, she wanted to check it out right now, but she'd needed to be patient. If her hunch was right, she had a pretty good idea who took the whale statue and why. She still didn't know where it was and had no idea how she would figure that out, but she'd think of something.

Having done all she could do for now, she finished the rest of her lunch and as many of Ben's french fries as she could steal. A girl needed her strength. In spite of missing whale statues, they still had a bridge to decorate!

A couple of hours later, the candy cane and whale decorations were hung on the light poles and the Depoe Bay bridge was festively adorned with the full, fresh, green cedar wreaths she and Ben had helped put together with the other local volunteers in Anna and Ken's garage. Logan was surprised at how satisfying and warm it felt to be part of the community that made it happen. These were good people.

All she had to do now was find a fifteen-foot missing baby whale statue before the tree-decorating ceremony on Saturday.

9:00 A.M.
MONDAY, NOVEMBER 27

The NewsTimes receptionist was a stickler for the rules—no one but employees were allowed past the front desk without an escort, so when Sam pulled up front, she saw that Melissa had parked Logan in one of the uncomfortable plastic bucket chairs in the lobby. Canned Christmas music drifted out when she opened the front door.

Sam made it up to Logan with the coffee and donuts she had squirreled away in her large messenger bag. Once they were out of earshot and view of the receptionist, Sam passed a thermos and two of the donuts to Logan and dropped her off at the bottom of the rickety stairs that led up to the Morgue.

"That should fuel your hunt. Just don't get anything on anything," she warned as she walked back to her desk, "or Melissa will have my hide."

Sam had a phone interview she couldn't reschedule but promised—or threatened—she'd be back in an hour to find out what Logan was looking for. Logan had been evasive but assured her that if she found anything, she'd be the first to know.

"If there's a story here, I want it!" Sam said.

After revving her engine with sugar, grease, and caffeine, Logan wiped her hands and got to work. She scanned the spines of the binders, trying to remember which one held what she was looking for. She pulled down the ones covering the 1960s, brought them back to the table, and settled in.

Finally, she found it.

NewsTimes
October 1969
Ambassador To Bring Art to Depoe Bay

Logan skim-read the article. Ambassador William Elliot, whose most recent posting had been in Rome, was planning on retiring in the area in a few years. Over the course of his career, William Elliot and his wife, Donna, had accumulated a large private collection of art. They told the reporter they planned on sharing a good portion of their collection with the public. Plans for a unique museum to showcase the paintings, sculptures, and tapestries—similar to the one Hearst had donated to California, but on a smaller scale—were in the works. The wife's sister lived in Lincoln City and that's how they had discovered this unique, coastal paradise.

It was the photo that accompanied the story that interested Logan. A trim, handsome man with salt and pepper hair, wearing a suit that fit him perfectly, stood next to a stylish, conservatively dressed woman. Both had warm smiles and posed with their hands lying loosely but protectively on the slim shoulders of their son, eleven-year-old Charles William Elliot, who gazed distractedly at something in the distance behind the photographer.

Yes!

When Sam arrived, Logan showed her the article and photo, and explained her far-out thinking, but quickly added, "This doesn't mean anything; it's a stretch, I know."

Sam agreed it was worth tracking down and knew exactly where to start. She had to work but told Logan to get down to the county assessor's office. Logan pulled it up on her phone, got directions, and told Sam she would keep her posted.

If Logan's theory panned out, Sam would definitely get the scoop on this one.

Chapter 9

TUESDAY, NOVEMBER 28
7:00 A.M. FOGARTY BEACH

Sam was right, the county assessor's office had property cards with the records of deed transfers going back to 1960, but they were indexed by assessor's map and tax lot number, so they hadn't done Logan much good. The assessor was very helpful, though, and said the County Clerk's Office index would probably have what she needed. Plus, she could search online. If the Elliots had purchased any property in anticipation of retiring here, or after actually retiring, and the deed was recorded, it would be in there.

Deeds were sorted by year, so Logan was excited when she found it without too much effort. There it was in plain black and white. The Elliots had bought property in Lincoln County in 1971!

But almost immediately her hopes fell. The legal description of the property was written in such confusing terms that Logan couldn't figure out where it was. Lincoln County covered a lot of ground. Without an address, her little Sherlock Holmes investigation was dead in the water.

The assessor's office came to the rescue again and said to bring a copy of the deed to them in the morning and they'd help her translate it into plain English. The office didn't open until 9:00 a.m., so she had plenty of time for a morning run. By the time she'd pulled on some clothes and tied her shoes, Dixon was waiting at the door, panting in happy anticipation. The labraheeler was always ready for a run, and since she'd be gone most of the day, Logan decided to put in an extra mile or two this morning to wear him out. When they got to the highway, she headed north toward Fogarty Beach, three miles away.

When they jogged past the empty ring where the whale statue had been, Logan's thoughts turned to where the little guy was now and what to do about it if it was where she thought it might be. But she shut those thoughts down as she picked up speed. First, she had to get the address. One step at a time. When they arrived at Fogarty Beach, Logan started looking for a stick to throw for a game of fetch. It was one of Dixon's favorite things to do. Just then, a magnificent white dog ran up to them, barking happily, tail high and waving like a flag. After the two dogs sniffed each other, the dog did a few play bows, barked loudly, inviting Dixon to play. Dixon looked at Logan for permission and when she nodded, he took off down the sand in a merry game of chase. Even though the white dog was stocky and low to the ground, he was surprisingly fast and agile, keeping up with Dixon's every pivot.

Logan recognized the breed at once. Julie, her neighbor back in Jasper, CA got an English Cream Golden Retriever for her three-year old daughter a few years back. The girl named him Marshmallow, but since she couldn't pronounce his full name, she called him Marmo and that's the name that stuck.

The owner of this English Cream, a man in his sixties, jogged over and apologized for his dog's enthusiastic behavior. "Sorry about that—Jake loves everybody! I know we're not supposed to, but I bring him down here and let him run off leash as long as no one's here. I was just about to hook him up when he saw your dog. Thanks for letting them play together."

"No problem at all," Logan said. "Dixon's a rescue and it's always good to let him play with other dogs. Even though he's almost three years old, the vet says it helps socialize him. How old's your dog?"

"About a year and a half," the man said. "I'm glad you've got a male. We waited as long as we could, but Jake's getting snipped next week and not a moment too soon. The vet says he'll calm down some once he's neutered."

He reached his hand out to shake Logan's, "I'm Lenny, by the way."

"Logan," she said. "Nice to meet you—and Jake."

They found a large driftwood log to sit on and for the next fifteen minutes, they watched the two dogs run through the surf, chase each other up, around, and over various pieces of driftwood and rocks.

Like a proud grandfather, Lenny showed Logan pictures of Jake's first and only litter, a squirming pile of four-week-old, cute puppies, some cream and some a darker, reddish gold. A traditional, female Golden Retriever lived next door and Jake had managed to fit in a date with her before getting fixed.

Just then, both dogs ran up and plopped down happily in front of their owners' feet, panting heavily. Lenny put his phone away and reached into his backpack for a large collapsible bowl and a bottle of water. He filled the bowl and placed it between the two dogs, who took turns noisily lapping up their cool drink. Traffic was picking up on the highway, so Logan said their goodbyes and thanked Lenny again for the impromptu doggie play date and sharing his dog's water with Dixon. They took it easy on the return trip but were still home in plenty of time for Logan to shower and drive to the assessor's office in Newport.

Like the Blues Brothers, she was on a mission!

Chapter 10

GORDIE

The winter sky morphed from charcoal to a pale, pearl gray over the treetops behind the big house. Gordie watched his breath fog in the cold air and stomped his feet to keep his toes warm. He needed better boots, but with the baby coming, he and Ramona were saving every dime.

Yesterday, he had finally gotten Ramona to let him spend the money to take her to a doctor in Newport for a checkup. The doctor said all was well and gave them a due date of May 26. Gordie's stomach had clenched a bit with the firm date. He was thrilled they were going to have a child, but this meant they only had six months to scrape together enough for the hospital bill, not counting the doctor's appointments in the meantime, which he would make sure Ramona kept. Plus, they needed to save first-and-last month's rent for an apartment in town.

There just wasn't enough space in the tiny trailer for a baby, and even though Charlie had offered them a room in the big house, Ramona had absolutely put her foot down. Charlie was often generous, but they had no formal employment with him and basically just got room and board. They couldn't rely on him remembering to pay them. They needed a stable income now that they were going to be a family.

A young couple they had met at the Mexican market in Newport and become friends with told them their apartment may be available when their lease was up in a few months. They invited them for dinner last night and when it got late and a storm was heading in, told them they could stay over so they wouldn't have to drive back in the rain. Gordie decided it would do Ramona good to have a night off, so he'd called Charlie and told him he'd be back first thing in the morning.

He explained that a storm was coming in, but Charlie said not to worry, he would be fine. In fact, he seemed happy about it. Said that worked out perfectly. Gordie hoped he had under- stood what he told him and wouldn't go wandering around in the storm. Charlie's grip on reality was definitely slipping more and more often.

Which was why Gordie was standing here outside at seven-thirty in the morning, shivering, waiting for his boss as instructed. He hoped Charlie had gone to bed last night or at least fallen asleep in his chair as he sometimes did. He'd know soon enough.

When another ten minutes had passed and his boss still had not come out, Gordie decided to check on him. Just as he was about to knock, Charlie swung the big front doors open wide and said, "Well, good morning, Gordie! Ready to see something special?"

The old guy looked fine. He hadn't looked this happy since the last time Ramona made tamales. His hair was combed, his eyes were clear, and his voice steady. Charlie looked and sounded absolutely normal. Maybe he was getting better. Maybe they had been worried about him for nothing.

"Absolutely, Charlie," Gordie said, relieved he was okay. "Lead the way."

Gordie followed his boss along a path that led around the north side of the large house to the back of the property. Whoever had built this place originally had designed it well.

For reasons Charlie never had been able or willing to explain, construction on the house had never been completed, and what was complete had not been maintained over the years, but it was solidly built and could have been a real beauty. It could be now if anyone had the time and money to put into it.

Someone had even cleared at least an acre out back behind the house for a pool. A low stone wall with fancy columns marked the boundaries of where the pool would have gone, but it had never been dug. Still, Charlie called it the Neptune Pool and referred to the property as "the Ranch," and he and Ramona's little travel trailer as one of the "casitas."

Whatever.

Gordie was anxious to see what Charlie was so excited about, but before they rounded the corner, Charlie made him tie a bandana around his head to cover his eyes. Maybe a piñata was part of the surprise. Gordie chuckled at the thought. Charlie guided him a few more steps in, then told him he could remove the bandana and open his eyes.

"Ta-da!"

Gordie blinked a couple of times, but no, he wasn't seeing things. He was standing nose to nose with a statue of a baby gray whale, its tail lifted jauntily into the air. The one he'd seen mounted in front of the seawall in Depoe Bay.

"Well?" Charlie said, beaming with pride. "What do you think? Isn't he gorgeous! Absolutely one of the best representations of Classical Greek sculpture I've found. See the realism? The attention to detail? Perfectly proportioned . . . Those Greeks knew what they were about. I think we should mount it right over there, overlooking the south side of the pool. Leaving it at this height, of course. At this level, it looks as if his eye is following you "

While the old man walked the perimeter and rambled on about his latest acquisition for his art collection and when they could start public tours, all Gordie could do was wonder how Charlie had

While the old man walked the perimeter and rambled on about his latest acquisition for his art collection and when they could start public tours, all Gordie could do was wonder how Charlie had managed to get it here.

He couldn't have lifted it by himself—the thing must weigh two or three hundred pounds. Gordie racked his brain. Charlie's place was off the beaten path, and he hardly ever went into town. Who could he have hired to help him? And who would have agreed to steal a public sculpture in the first place?

Then he remembered.

Scotty. Scotty and Bart must have come by yesterday to haul off the big pile of yard debris he'd stacked up after clearing out some blackberry brambles that had taken over half the yard and grown up and around the foundation. He had forgotten he'd scheduled a pickup a few days ago.

Scotty had a monster truck big enough for the job. Those two would do anything for cash, and Charlie must have offered them enough to make it worth the risk of getting arrested. They must have stolen the statue last night while he and Ramona were in Newport.

Damn. Now what was he going to do?

Chapter 11

While Gordie was gathering his thoughts and trying to figure out how he was going to get this statue returned to its proper spot in Depoe Bay without getting himself or Charlie arrested, he heard someone coming around the side of the house.

"Mr. Elliot?" a woman's voice called out. "Mr. Charles Elliot? I knocked on the door, but no one answered."

Gordie's heart sank. He tried to intercept the woman before she saw the stolen statue. But he couldn't get his legs to move fast enough.

Before he got two feet, a tall, athletic woman with long, coppery hair came breezing around the corner. Her green eyes took in the whole scene at a glance: Gordie, Charlie, and the whale sculpture. To her credit, she only hesitated for a moment, then with a friendly smile, walked over to Charlie.

"Mr. Charles Elliot?" she said, reaching out her hand to the older man.

Elliot? He and Ramona had wondered what his last name was.

Charlie didn't skip a beat.

"Ahhh, Julia! You're just in time . . . and you're such a kidder. Come here, my girl," he said, enveloping the woman in a bear hug. The woman went along with this, although Gordie doubted her name was Julia. He'd never seen her before.

Charlie took his guest by the hand and practically dragged her over to a spot along the east edge of the stone wall. "Right here, I think? Don't you? I know it doesn't fit completely in with your original drawings for the Neptune Pool, but you know me, always changing things at La Cuesta Encantada. You know how I like to keep you on your toes, Julia," he chuckled, then called back over his shoulder.

"Gordie! Why don't you see if that lovely wife of yours can rustle us up some breakfast? Or brunch, rather, by the time we're done here. Julia and I have a lot of ground to cover first!" Gordie stumbled back to the travel trailer and filled Ramona in. She said she'd do this one meal, but they really needed to have a talk about what to do with Charlie as soon as the woman, whoever she was, left. Like Gordie, Ramona was also curious about why the stranger was going along with Charlie's delusions.It just didn't make any sense. Maybe she knew something they didn't.

They'd picked up some groceries on the way back from Newport, so Ramona whipped up a good meal, including one of Charlie's favorites, chilaquiles with slices of ripe avocado and lots of hot sauce, accompanied by strong, black coffee, which the woman said was delicious. She also put away her share of the chilaquiles.

Finally, Gordie convinced Charlie it was afternoon, not morning, and time for his siesta.

"You're welcome to stay here, Julia," Charlie said, "or you can stay in one of the casitas, whichever you prefer. I know I've given you a lot of work to do, so take your time. See you tonight at dinner!" he added as he allowed Gordie to herd him up the stairs to his room.

When the two men were out of earshot, Ramona pressed a napkin against her eyelids and looked at Logan apologetically. The wavy-haired woman seemed to take it all in stride.

Smiling, she said, "Hi, Ramona. I'm Logan McKenna. Nice to meet you."

Gordie came back downstairs and introduced himself, too. "Good to meet you, Logan. You handled all of that really well. I hope you can forgive Charlie; he means no harm; he just gets a little confused sometimes. I don't know why he kept calling you Julia . . . ," he said.

"Well," Logan said, "I might be able to clear that up. It fits with everything I know so far. Julia Morgan was the architect who teamed with William Hearst to build Hearst Castle in San Simeon, CA." Ramona and Gordie looked at her blankly.

"Hearst often referred to it as "the Ranch" or "La Cuesta Encantada," and Julia Morgan helped him design not only the main house, but the casitas or guest houses, too," Logan said.

Ramona was the first to catch on. "Charlie thinks he's William Hearst?" she asked.

"And this rundown place is Hearst Castle?" Gordie said, spreading his arms and looking askance at their surroundings.

"Well, I'm not sure what Charlie thinks; he seems to be mixing up a few facts," Logan said. "But I think it's something like that. His parents collected art, including Classical Greek sculptures."

She told them about discovering that the whale statue was missing when they went to decorate the town for Christmas, then showed them a copy of the newspaper article with the picture of Charlie and his parents when his father was inter- viewed by the local paper in 1969.

"Wow, Charlie's father was an ambassador?" Gordie said.

"But what happened to them?" Ramona asked, "His parents, I mean? And how did you find him? And this place? How did you know where he lived?"

"My friend, Sam, is a reporter. She did some digging and discovered Mr. and Mrs. Elliot both died in a train crash in Italy when Charlie was twenty-one," she said. "It was a last-minute trip to collect some ancient Greek and Roman sculptures. They bought this land here in Oregon and had begun to build the house and other features, part of which they planned on opening to the public as an art museum. Similar to Hearst Castle, but not as large. They were in the middle of all that when they went on their trip."

"Why wasn't Charlie with them?" Ramona asked. "In this picture of him as a little boy, you can see he is not quite right. Why would they leave him alone, even when he got older?"

"According to Sam's research, Charlie was never enrolled in the public schools here. His parents hired a private tutor and caregiver for him," Logan said. "A man named Victor Klein. Back in the sixties, if you had a child with special needs, people usually kept it secret. People didn't talk about mental or physical disabilities or differences back then."

"Maybe Mr. Klein knows more," Gordie said. "Is he still alive?"

"I don't know what happened to him or how long he stayed after Charlie's parents died," Logan said. "The trail on Klein seems to have gone cold, but to answer your original question, the local assessor helped me track down this address. I took a long shot and drove out to see if by some chance the little boy in the picture had grown up and was still living here."

Ramona sat back, taking all this in.

"How sad," she said. "Charlie must have been so confused when his parents didn't come back, and then when Klein left, he was all alone. How awful not to have any family. No wonder he is . . . like he is."

"Well," Logan said, "he might still have some family left."

"Who?" Gordie asked. "We've asked him if he has any family, but he's never mentioned anyone."

"Sam found an aunt. She used to live in Lincoln City, that's how the Elliots first discovered Depoe Bay and fell in love with the Oregon coast—from visiting her. The woman's name was Angie Brewster. They moved back to Colorado, where her husband was from, when he became sick. He passed away and the aunt has since died, but her son, Charlie's first cousin, might still be alive. I wanted to wait until I made sure this Charles Elliot was the right Charles Elliot before trying to contact him.

"It's a wonder Charlie has made it on his own all these years," Gordie said. "Other than getting things mixed up more and more frequently, he seems to be pretty healthy."

"Well, according to Sam's research, Charlie's parents had a trust and left the property to him, along with a sizeable chunk of cash. His mind was probably clearer when he was younger, but knowing their son's limitations, his parents made sure to set everything up so that the bank served as the trustee and nothing changed for Charlie when Klein left. The property was paid for, as well as a brand new truck. The bank made sure things like taxes, utilities, and monthly living expenses for Charlie were all paid out of the trust."

"That answers a lot of questions," Gordie said, "but it doesn't get us any closer to solving the problem sitting out in the back- yard. Charlie may think he's William Hearst and that whale statue is his latest purchase of ancient Greek art for the Neptune Pool, but the City of

Depoe Bay won't see it that way."

"I agree," Logan said, pushing her chair away from the table. "Why don't you let me help you clear the dishes and clean up? We can brainstorm solutions while we're working. I always think better when I'm on my feet."

*****

The mystery of the missing whale statue had been solved, but the solution to Charlie's problems was a Gordian knot. The first order of business was to find a way to return the whale statue and keep Charlie out of jail. Thanks to Bill and Mosely, they had managed to accomplish both. They quietly loaded the whale statue into Bill's truck one night and put it back where it belonged. Mosely's job with the City of Depoe Bay hadn't hurt. When he had explained what had happened and that this was a result of an old man's confused state of mind, the city was glad not to press charges, as long as the statue was returned unscathed. They'd made a brief statement on their website about it being sent out for repair, which luckily, no one questioned. It had been reinstalled and was now properly festooned with Christmas wreaths and ribbons as it should be.

Logan and Sam then tracked down Charlie's long lost cousin, Donnie Brewster, who was delighted to discover Charlie was still alive and to reconnect with him.

Gordie and Ramona continued to care for Charlie, even though Gordie had to take over the cooking duties for a few weeks while Ramona powered through the worst bouts of morning sickness. Other than a baby bump, you'd never know she was five months pregnant— she had more energy than ever. After weeks of brainstorming and video conferencing with Charlie's cousin, an initial plan was made, just in time for Christmas.

Chapter 12

TWO MONTHS LATER CHRISTMAS EVE DAY

Logan set the long dining room table for fifteen, while Gordie lit the fire in the huge fireplace and ensured the beautifully decorated, fragrant Douglas fir in the corner was secure in its stand. With dogs and children coming, it was a wise move.

Wonderful aromas emanated from the kitchen, where Ramona and Ben had been cooking all day. There were dishes to please everyone: clove-studded ham, scalloped potatoes, crisp Brussel sprouts, green beans almondine, three kinds of salad, prime rib, nine kinds of olives, fresh-baked dinner rolls, and even mac and cheese for the kids. And, of course, desserts! Ramona made flan and Ben built a triple-decker spice cake with cream cheese frosting along with a flourless chocolate cake and ice cream for the glutonians.

As dinner guests arrived, each placed their Christmas gifts under the tree, Logan took their coats, and Gordie manned the bar. There had been a few showers earlier, but the night was clear, and a generous, gibbous moon could be seen out of the windows, silhouetting the treetops, blessing the gathering.

Earlier this morning, Ben and Gordie had decked the halls with cedar boughs, filled a large basket with cinnamon-scented pinecones by the fire, and Anna and Ken brought two giant, fresh cedar wreaths for the front doors. Ken's ankle was healing, but Anna had to keep reminding him to use his crutches. He wasn't supposed to put too much weight on it, yet, but Ken was not known for following doctor's orders.

Sam came in pushing nine-month-old Magnolia in her stroller with one hand and pulling in a cooler filled with fresh crab with the other, stopping every few steps to push her glasses back up. Laughing, Logan went to help. This being prime crab- bing season, Sam's husband, Tim, a commercial fisherman, was out on their boat, the Sara Lynn, but he would try to make it in tomorrow for Christmas Day at least.

Once she got Sam a beer and Miss Magnolia some peeled apple slices to gnaw on, Logan poured herself a glass of cabernet and took stock of the room. By a minor miracle—in spite of a storm that threatened to snow in the airport—everyone was here, including

Charlie's cousin, Donnie Brewster, and his wife, Patty. They'd flown in from Colorado yesterday, bringing with them three of their grandchildren, the brave souls! The oldest, fourteen-year-old Lucas was a serious-minded young man whose bright carrot top was hard to miss in the melee. His brother, Jesse, the energetic eight-year-old towhead, was currently chasing Dixon around the table, trying to get his gloves back. And Mary Beth, the six-year-old with a head of springy, light-brown curls, was sitting very still by the stroller, totally enraptured with Miss Magnolia, who cooed and gurgled on cue, gripping Mary Beth's finger tightly in her little fist.

The last guests to arrive were Mosely and Bill. For keeping Charlie out of trouble and returning the whale, they were the official guests of honor. Logan watched as Charlie held court by the Christmas tree, shaking packages to guess what was in them. Freshly shaved, with a new haircut and new clothes, he looked like a new man. And this was one of his good days. He seemed to know who he and everyone else was, and he hadn't called her Julia even once all day.

Finding Charlie's cousin had not been hard at all. Donnie Brewster, Angie's son, had stayed in Colorado after his parents died. He met and married Patty, and they'd raised two boys on a working cattle ranch. They'd lost one of their sons, but the other had married and given them the three grandchildren who were here now.

The sisters had become estranged shortly after Angie had moved with her family back to Colorado, so the cousins had lost touch and never knew each other as adults. While he had distant memories of his cousin as a child, he did not know the extent of Charlie's limitations, nor even that he had moved to Oregon. When he'd learned about the situation, Donnie had hopped on the first plane out to meet Charlie. When he arrived, he quickly assessed the situation and had worked out a temporary game plan, involving Charlie as much as possible.

He and Patty had been involved with a local program that helped special needs children and adults work with certain horses on the ranch, so they weren't fazed by Charlie's way of looking at the world.

The plan was for Gordie and Ramona to be hired as full-time caretakers for Charlie, as well as making their unofficial jobs as groundskeeper and cook permanent positions, with good salaries, health insurance, and a generous 401K. Funds were provided to bring the house up to code, including converting the back half of the house into a generous living area for Gordie and Ramona and the baby that was on the way.

They were even going to work with Charlie to create a sculpture garden out back. When and if the time came that Charlie needed more assistance than they could provide, Donnie and Patty said they had plenty of room back at their ranch in Colorado. They'd be frequent visitors until then.

Just then, a flushed Ramona popped her head out of the kitchen and called everybody to dinner. Logan helped Ben and Ramona bring out the food and light the candles set along the center of the table.

When they were all seated, Charlie stood and thanked everyone for coming, then raised his glass and with a tear in his eye made a heartfelt, if not wholly original toast, from one of his favorite Christmas movies.

"God bless us, everyone!" "Here! Here!"

"Salut!"

"Now, everybody, please eat before your food gets cold!" Ramona said, taking a seat next to Gordie, and starting the serving dishes around the table.

Logan had no trouble doing as instructed. Everything was delicious.

Chapter 13

An hour later, stuffed to the gills, most of the dinner guests looked ready to take a nap, but the children wanted to open their

Christmas gifts, so the adults rallied. Everyone helped clear the table and then pulled their chairs over to gather around the tree, leaving a little space in front for Charlie, who was playing Santa, sitting cross-legged on the floor to pass out presents.

Dixon stretched out in front of the fire, taking that nap everyone wanted. He'd managed to get himself generously fed under the table by almost everyone.

Since there were going to be so many people, they had done a Secret Santa gift exchange, with a reasonable dollar limit.

A month ago, Logan had put everyone's name in a hat and drawn random names; she'd told each person their giftee. Sam got Ben's name but as she was already in on the secret, it saved Logan from having to cheat to make sure she got Ben's name.

As the pile of presents under the tree grew smaller, Logan could hardly contain her excitement. It was all she could do to keep a look of calm detachment on her face. She oohed and ahhed appropriately over Mary Beth's live butterfly kit and the handmade baby quilt Mosley had made for Ramona's bun in the oven. Apparently, his mother had been a star quilter and he'd picked it up from her.

Finally, all the gifts were distributed, and Charlie got up to mingle and try on his new North Face jacket Ramona had gotten for him at the outlet mall. He didn't seem to realize that one person still hadn't received a gift. Ben.

Ben sat there awkwardly for a minute, then got up to go into the kitchen, mumbling something about setting up the dessert table, but Logan reached up, grabbed his elbow, and pulled him back down. "You may want to wait for this, hon," she said, grinning.

Just then, everyone heard frantic scrabbling sounds coming from the living room. Dixon roused himself from his nap, lifted his head, and became totally focused on the open doorway, waiting.

He didn't have to wait long. In the next second, a big, fluffy, cream-colored puppy came galumphing around the corner, dragging

Sam behind him at the end of a blue nylon leash. Exuberant but looking a little confused, he made a beeline for the big, calm, steady-looking guy in the room who'd been working in the kitchen all day and smelled like food.

When he made it to Ben, he dove under his chair, turned himself around, then popped his head out and looked up at his protector, wriggling his whole body joyously, barking a couple of times for good measure.

The puppy had definitely chosen his human!

Dixon came over to sniff the newcomer, approved, and then went to lie down by Logan's chair.

Logan had initially hesitated to pick out a dog for Ben, but a few weeks ago, when she and Ben had gone on a morning run together down to Fogarty Beach, they'd bumped into Lenny, who was there with Jake, his gorgeous English Cream Golden Retriever. It was love at first sight.

The breed was such a perfect fit for Ben. Strong and athletic, but gentle and calm. This time Logan remembered to get Lenny's contact information. She called later that day, as soon as Ben was outside for a few minutes, and whispered into the phone asking Lenny if all the puppies were spoken for yet. He said he had two male puppies left, both healthy with great personalities. After reassuring him that Ben was an experienced dog owner and knew how to raise a puppy, Lenny was delighted to reserve the largest male for him and be part of the holiday surprise.

Logan was usually terrible at keeping secrets, but the look on Ben's face when he nuzzled his puppy's neck and let the dog lick him all over his face made her very happy that she'd kept this one.

Everyone, it seemed, was overflowing with emotion. So many good things had come to pass in the last few weeks—it was hard to take it all in.

"Merry Christmas, honey!" Logan said. "What are you going to name him?"

All the dinner guests got in the spirit and started shouting suggestions.

"Polar Bear!"
"Sasquatch!"
"Love Bug!"
"Mr. Wiggles!"

Then Samson, Donnie's eight-year-old grandson, raised his hand like he was in school.

"His hair's the same color as yours, Mr. McKenna," he said. "How about Blondie?"

Ben's last name was Halvard, but he didn't bother correcting the boy. A lot of people assumed he and Logan had the same last name and he didn't mind a bit.

"You can't name him Blondie," Lucas whispered, pointing with an air of superiority to the puppy's undersides. "Blondie's a girl's name and this one's a *male* dog!"

"Hmmm . . . ," Ben said, dutifully considering everyone's suggestions.

Looking into the dog's big, solemn eyes, he asked, "What do you want to be called, little guy?"

Everyone looked at the puppy, as if he might actually answer the question.

Then Sam looked up from her phone, where she had been scrolling and shouted, "Finn! It's perfect! It says here that Finn means fair-haired in Gaelic. He's certainly fair-haired."

"And it sounds gender-neutral to me," she added, smiling at the boys.

"What do you think?" Ben asked his dog.

"Wiggles, Sasquatch, Polar Bear, Love Bug, or Finn? Choose wisely, you're going to be stuck with this name for many years."

The puppy stopped wriggling for half a second and everyone held their breath, then he gave one joyful bark.

"That was a one-syllable bark!" Ben said. "Finn it is!"

Author Bios

Kyra Blank

Contributions(s):
Of the Mist

Bio

Kyra Blank is an Author, Youth Pastor, and Sheep Rancher living on the Oregon Coast. She has a Bachelors of Arts in English from Oregon State University, and has a background in Newspaper Journalism. Kyra spends her free time writing, exploring the natural world, and reading historical fiction in the field with her Valais Blacknose Sheep. Kyra was previously published in The Corvallis Advocate and Prism Magazine, and is working on completing her first fantasy novel. She lives on a multi-generational ranch in Oregon with her husband, parents, their pomeranian Hugo and many other animals.

Follow her on Instagram @redhairedshepherdess for up-to-date publishing information and inquiries.

Valerie Davisson

Contributions(s):
Whale of a Christmas Crime

Bio

A self-admitted book addict, Valerie was the kid with the flashlight under her pillow, reading long after lights out. A life of travel led to degrees in Anthropology and a pervasive interest in people. She lives in Depoe Bay with her husband, John, and their golden retriever, Finn.

When not out immersing herself in nature, walking on the beach or exploring the forest, she can be found working on her latest book. And if she's not at her keyboard, she is probably in the kitchen, cooking up a storm for family and friends.

Valerie Davisson is the author of the Amazon best-selling, 9-book Logan McKenna Mystery Series set mainly here on the Oregon coast, several novellas, a poetry book, and a non-fiction book, Saturday Salon: Bringing Conversation and Community Back Into Our Lives. To learn more about Valerie and her books, check out her website: valeriedavisson.com

Maizey Gardiner

Contributions(s):
*Secrets of Those Lost
to the Sea*

Bio

Maizey Gardiner lives to tell stories, through poems, songs, short stories even through theater and dance. When she's not writing, you can find her in the local youth theater, competing on her cheer team, or curled up with a cozy quilt, a cup of tea, and a good book. She aspires to one day become a pilot, though surviving 5th grade is the more immediate goal.

Publisher's Note: Maizey was the standout member of the short lived, and now defunct Sterncastle Youth Writing Collective. As a testament to her talent and commitment to the craft of writing, her story has been accepted here amongst the work of our adult authors. We look forward to great things from this up and coming author.

Savannah Gardiner

Contributions(s):
The Guest Book

Bio

Savannah Gardiner is a PNW native, grateful to be back to her roots, born in Portland, raised in the Puget Sound before living in Utah and Hawaii. Savannah grew up in community theater and learned the need for storytelling at an early age. She married her high school sweetheart and together they have one son and three daughters, along with a BBQ restaurant right here on the Oregon Coast.

Jill Hagen

Contributions(s):
Sacred Creek Song
Whittling

Bio

Jill Hagen, a Native American elder, was raised on a reservation in upstate New York. Her writings and her art reflect her cultural influences. Jill believes many snippets strung together form a life. Her upcoming memoir *Snippets & Vinegar* is a slice of life with the bitter and acidic parts included. In her opinion it could be seen as either a 'how to or how not to' book.

She was born into a matriarchal/matrilinear society. There was sexual and physical abuse, food allergies, teenage pregnancy, reunion 40 years later, racism, and spiritual gifts. Her memoir also addresses learning disabilities and undiagnosed ADD with hyperactivity, as well as overcoming mental health concerns. Grief was almost constant throughout her life with the loss of animals, friends, husband, daughter, siblings and parents.

Visiting Western doctor's offices seldom happened because her mother was a traditional tribal herbalist. Often, the awful

taste of the herbal medicine alone was enough to make her well. The knowledge of traditional herbal healings had been passed down through generations. This was a special gift that often took the family into the woods spring and autumn to forage.

In spite of issues in public elementary and high schools including being a drop out, Jill attended 8 colleges and universities. She eventually attained a two-year professional master's degree. Her natural curiosity lead her to move 23 times around 5 different states. Her education continues as long as her heart, mind, and spirit are willing to listen.

Linoa Linette

Contributions(s):
The Seagull
Bigfoot Saves Jesse

Bio

While Linoa Linette has lived in many places across the United States, including Wisconsin, Maine, and Idaho, she is proud to call the beautiful Oregon Coast her true 'home'. When she is not writing or creating digital art for her upcoming horror series *Perpetua: The North Iron Star,* she is enjoying the beach with her husband and two pups, Ripley and Maf. She also enjoys world building in the more forgiving universe of *The Sims*, and is coming ever closer to the impressive feat of completing a living 'dex in *Pokemon Home*.

Tim O'Brien

Contributions(s):
My Name Is John

Bio

Born in New Jersey, I graduated from Susquehanna Community High School in Northeastern Pennsylvania. I attended Penn State, and SUNY Binghamton. I've spent most of my life in Colorado. We raised a family, learned to ski and climb. I've had two amazing careers; I ran nightclubs in downtown Denver, and seafood departments for Kroger's Denver affiliate, King Soopers. I live with my wife, Susan and our dog Valentine in the hills outside of Toledo Oregon. We call it the Shire. I spend my free time reading, writing, and walking the Oregon Coast's wreck line.

Brenda Buchanan Saltzer

Contributions(s):
This Enchanted Place

Bio

Brenda Buchanan Saltzer loves connecting people and causes, and is a champion of women of all ages. She has devoted more than 25 years to women-centered family advocacy and as a legislative consultant for family and children's support issues. Through her company, Reimagine Best, she helps dreamers launch their great ideas and overcome life's setbacks. Brenda is the author of, *Adopting a Family for You: A Love Story,* through which she hopes to help change the perception surrounding birth mothers and adoption. Brenda lives with her husband, Brian on the enchanted Oregon Coast. She has three kindhearted daughters and four perfect grandchildren. She loves people, adventure, reading, traveling, and coming back home.

Leah Shrifter

Contributions(s):
Rose In Fairyland
Truth

Bio

Leah Shrifter is an author and musician. As a child, she told herself stories when she listened to music—and never grew out of it. That is how she came to write *The Sky Dwellers* and later the prequel, *Seed of the Gods*. She also writes short stories, poems and memoirs which she enjoys reading on public radio. As a professional violinist, her favorite gig is musical theater, telling stories with music, singing, and dancing.

She lives near the ocean with her husband and their two cats.

Joe C. Smolen

Contributions(s):
Skinny Boy
A Mere Slip of a Girl
D.C. Chester

Bio

Joe C. Smolen is a Pacific Northwest author with Seattle, Portland, and Oregon Coast affections. While his B.A. English is of the University of Washington, his post-grad work is just fiction, the pubbed of which – along with his bent – are reviewable at joecsmolen.com

Joe might tell you "Writing a good story feels just like surfing the Solar Wind."

Under his by-line "L.W. Smolen", Joe tells stories in two voices – one juvenilely picaresque, the other a crisp and direct literary. Like Willa Cather never feeling she bested **My Antonia**, his current novel is being written in the shadow of his much-loved novel **Lostine.**

With the ghost of their black Standard Poodle, *Rico Suave*, he and his wife Sherrie live on the Oregon Coast in a Prairie-style house they built themselves.

About Sterncastle
Writer's Collective

Sterncastle Writer's Collective is a unique (perhaps one-of-a-kind) partnership between a writer's group and a publishing house. Our membership runs the gamut from hobbyist writers who do it for the love the art to seasoned authors who have published multiple books. The Collective meets monthly to learn and grow as authors through lessons, workshops, and writing challenges. Our primary strength is in providing each other with much needed feedback on our projects through our regular read and critique sessions.

This book is the first publication of Sterncastle Writer's Collective and we look forward to producing an entirely new group anthological work each year. All expenses for the production of this volume have been underwritten by Sterncastle Publishing.

For information about how to establish a Sterncastle Writer's Collective in your area please contact Sterncastle Publishing via email at: community@sterncastlepublishing.org

Made in United States
Troutdale, OR
12/21/2023